LABOR SPY

Labor Spy

BY

GT-99

THE BOBBS-MERRILL COMPANY
Publishers

INDIANAPOLIS   NEW YORK

CONTENTS

CONTENTS—*Continued*

LABOR SPY

LABOR SPY

CHAPTER 1

"Confidential"

MACHINISTS—Young, single, well-educated, willing to travel, confidential. Y-624.

THE ad was in the paper on Sunday; I noticed it again Wednesday; and then it ran on the following Saturday and Sunday. It sounded rather queer. "Confidential"? Why shouldn't the company give its address just as other firms did when they advertised for shop men? Then, too, education and willingness to travel were odd requirements for a machinist.

The fourth time the ad appeared, I sent a telegram to the box number saying, "WANT MACHINIST'S JOB AND HAVE PLENTY OF WHAT IT TAKES," and gave my name, address and phone number. It cost me thirty-four cents, but I was playing a hunch, and thought a wire would make quite a splash.

Although it was over twenty years ago, I can still see the ad in the "Help Wanted, Male," page of the paper. I can still see the red-haired man who took my wire. He was

[11]

35307

standing at the counter looking at a newspaper with a lot of war pictures. We talked about the war for a few minutes. Then he crabbed about his wife's wanting to go to her mother's house for the day, and he'd had to work, and she'd gone alone.

It's no wonder I remember. This telegram was to bring me a job that lasted over twenty years, a job that took me all over the country, caused me to have gray hair at thirty, and gave me more influence over my fellow man than that of a Supreme Court justice. It made me a politician, an accomplished liar, a successful public speaker; it gave me a number in place of a name; and, in the end, made me a wanderer on the face of the earth. It put me into the most fascinating and dangerous job in the world—it made me a labor spy.

Well, I sent the wire and went to the ball park. The Athletics won, with Bender pitching, and Home Run Baker hitting another one; and all in all it was a grand day. When I came home my landlady said, "A man called you. You were to call him back, no matter how late you came in." I phoned. It was about the ad, and the man who answered talked me into coming down to see him in the Bessemer Building right away. Sunday! Funny, wasn't it?

The office wasn't much to look at, no name on the door, and I was about to pass it up when I heard voices and walked in. A tall, skinny man asked me what I wanted, and then showed me into the next room where the Chief was sitting. I saw him a thousand times after that, and each time he would act much the same, looking at me with those pale blue eyes, and not moving at all. He could sit for hours with his elbows on the arms of his chair, perfectly straight until you'd think his back would break, his head bent forward a little and his hands clasped across his chest. The only time he moved was to write something or use the phone. The rest of the time he just sat there. Once in a long while he smiled, and it was worth waiting for because his face lit up all over and it made you glad to know someone who could smile like that.

He looked at me, and I looked at him, but finally I wilted. "Well," I said, fresh-like, "When do I start?"

He continued to look at me for another whole minute. I was trying to decide whether to get sore, or just leave, or what, when suddenly he smiled and said, "Son, it was nice of you to come in. Sit down." And I sat. His smile got me, just as I have seen it get hundreds of men since then. That minute I knew he was *my* boss and could have anything he wanted—and from that time on, he got it.

He started to talk, not prying into my affairs, but just conversational, and the first thing I knew, he had my whole story. All about my being born upstate and going to school there. About moving to the city with my family, and going to high school, and how father had made a little money, and then he and mother had decided to go back to the old country while I'd elected to stay here. Yes, they were Swiss—and I knew German, French and enough Italian to get by. He made a note of that, the only one he took. I had started to college, didn't like it, and had then become a machinist's apprentice for four years. And all about my working three years, on three different jobs, the job I had now, the patent I had applied for and my hopes of having a shop of my own.

The Chief asked me a lot of questions about machinery and kept referring to various kinds of work done on a line of lathes made in Indiana. They were common enough in my part of the country and I knew all about them.

Then he asked whether I belonged to a union, and if I had any friends who did, and if I had ever thought of joining a union, and if a union were a good thing for the workingman. I hadn't thought much about it, but I knew a few union men who belonged in order to receive the insurance benefits.

We chewed along like this for two hours, and at the end of it he knew my life history but I didn't know anything at all about him or that job I was applying for.

"Supposing you tell me about this job," I said suddenly.

He flashed that dead pan again, and I figured I had made him sore. He stared at me for the longest time, then grinned again and said, "All right, son, we'll talk about that. I have a job for you in another city. It's about four hundred miles away. The pay is forty-five cents an hour and they are working fifty-four hours a week. I'll pay your fare, and you can start right away. And there is a chance for you to make a dollar a day extra, every day in the month, by doing a little work on the side."

Then he asked me more about my education, and if I had

ever written much. I told him about writing for the school paper, and about the typewriter I had just bought, and that I wrote a long letter every week to my folks and every once in a while I wrote a piece about something or other and sent it to the contributor's column in the morning paper, and they had printed four of them.

"Well, that's fine," said the Chief. "Now I'll tell you what I want you to do for me. When you go on this job, you work in the shop just like the other men. But every day, I want you to write me a letter about your work. I want to know how the foreman treats you, how he treats the other men, what the other men have to say about the foreman and the superintendent and the general manager and the president. I want to know whether they are satisfied with the pay and working hours and working conditions. I want to know which men are always complaining, and also the ones who think it is a swell job and the best place in the world to work. I want to know whether any of the men waste material or loaf on the job or steal from the plant or from each other. If you have any ideas for improving production, let me know. I'm particularly interested in any efficiency suggestions you may have.

"Every day you are to write me a letter and tell me. Tell me what time you get to work in the morning, who you walk to work with and what he says. What you talk about with the foreman and the other men during the whole day. What you talk about at noon, and during the afternoon. And if you see any of them in the evening, talk to them

[15]

about the job and let me know what they think. I want their names, where they came from, whether they intend to stay or are looking for another job. Which side they favor in the war and why. How about it? Can you do that?"

"Sure I can do it," I replied after a minute, "but why?"

"Because you get a dollar a day extra for doing it," and the Chief looked me in the eye and went on steadily and slowly. "You get a dollar a day extra, and no one in the shop will know anything about it. You know it, and I know it, and the president of the company you are working for will know it, but none of the men you work with will know it.

"It's like this. The man who owns this shop has a lot of big orders to get out, war contracts. He has enough work to keep the place booming for at least two years. He wants to be *sure* his men are satisfied. If they should get dissatisfied and slow up production, or strike, he would lose a lot of money. The people who bought his goods would not get them on time and would sue him. The only way he can be positive about what's going on in the shop is to have someone there who lives and works right among the men and keeps him informed. You tell me—and I tell him. You know how working men are—they never tell the boss everything.

"That's what you are for—to tell us *everything* about the workmen and what they are thinking. You're a bright young fellow. You know the machinist's trade and you can talk well. You say you can write—and with me to help you and advise you, you will make a success of this, earn a lot of money and work your way into a swell job."

I was twenty-four, footloose, raring to go and here was a chance. I knew the plant he spoke of, and everyone had heard of the big contract they had just landed to make munitions for the Allies. I was a tough, hard kid; but there was a funny feeling inside me. And I had an odd metallic taste in my mouth as if two low-voltage wires were touching my tongue. Twice since then I have felt the same way. Once was in France, a few minutes after midnight on the morning of *the* September 26, and the other time will get into this story before I finish.

"When do I start?" I asked at last.

"Just as soon as I know a little more about the way you write," said the Chief. "I want you to go back to your job tomorrow as usual. When you get home at night, sit down at your typewriter and write me the story of your day's work, the talks you had with other men, any suggestions you have about the way things could be improved—just the same kind of a report I've been talking about. Bring this in to me tomorrow night about eight o'clock and if I find you can write well enough, you start right away."

I agreed and went home. I left him sitting just the same way as when I had come in and his face was dead serious again. He had smiled only twice, but these two times were worth remembering.

The next day I laid off and wrote a letter about a typical day at the shop. It was a honey, but I made it too good.

The Chief read it without saying a word. Finally he laughed and roared until the tears ran down his face. At last he said, "You're hired, hired in spite of this letter. You show you can write all right, but no shop in the country ever had so many things happen in a whole month, let alone a single day. On the level now, didn't you write up just about everything that happened since the time you started there?"

For a minute I thought about it; then I said, "Yes, I did. And I didn't go in at all today. I wanted this job, and I stayed home to write the report for you." You couldn't lie to the Chief.

"I knew it," and he laughed some more. "I'm glad you admitted it, but don't ever try anything like this again. You don't need to. And I'll never try to slip anything over either. You can count on that, and I'm going to count on you." He got out of his chair, came over to me and stuck out his hand. I shook it, looking right back into his funny blue eyes, and the deal was made. Not a scrap of writing, no contract—and we never needed one.

The next day I went to the plant and quit, got my tools, said good-by to my friends and took the midnight train. The Chief came down to see me off, and gave me a ticket, a sleeper, a sawbuck for expenses, and a few final suggestions.

"Now I've told you a lot and I can't expect you to remember it all," he finished. "We'll get that straightened out as we go along. If you forget it all, if you can't re-

[18]

member a single thing, try like blazes to think of this: no matter what happens, write the truth and nothing but the truth. If you aren't sure about something, say so. If you forget the exact details of some incident, don't be afraid to say you forgot. As time goes on, you may hold the jobs and lives of hundreds of men in your hands. If you don't know the Golden Rule, learn it, and apply it in your dealings with your associates, your employer and with me."

The Golden Rule! That was a funny one, I thought.

CHAPTER 2

First Report

THE plant was a lulu. Brand new, and with over a
thousand employees. Pretty big for that time. The
machine shop alone had more than a hundred men. All
I had to tell the employment man was where I had been
trained and he took me on, to start that same morning. The
pay was better than the chief had said: fifty cents an hour, ✓
fifty-four hours straight time, and six hours overtime at
time-and-a-half. Later I learned this was just like the
Chief. He wanted me to get a pleasant surprise by finding I had been given a better deal than I had expected.
This always had a good effect, making me anxious to stay
on the job and make good. These were big wages in those
days, the best I had ever made, and with a dollar a day extra
from the Chief I was sitting pretty.

I asked the employment man where I could get a room

and he told me to drop in at noon and he would have one for me. I said I'd like to be in a place with no other roomers. "I'll call a few places I know of and the one I take will be all right," he assured me. "The shop needs machinists badly and if you start right now, it will help out a lot. If you don't like the room I find for you, you can change in a day or two. I can give you a list and there are always a lot of places advertised in the papers." Nice friendly chap. He had a room for me when I came in at noon, and I lived there all the time I was on the assignment.

Walking over to the shop with the office boy, it occurred to me that I had been conducting myself just as if I had been on my own. Then I remembered this was just what the Chief had advised.

The foreman seemed to be a good egg, glad to see me as he was swamped with work and needed men. Within ten minutes, I was getting ready to set up a job on a big South Bend lathe. There were thirty lathes of all sizes in the shop, but only about half of them were in use. They hadn't been able to get machinists for the others.

My lathe was almost new and a beauty. I sharpened several tools, centered my job and started her up to make a good, full cut. The old girl shook once in a while, the way a lathe will, and the tool got pretty hot, but that was all pretty much as it should be.

I saw a few of the men looking at me strangely, and finally the foreman came up on the gallop. He shut off the

[21]

power and asked me what the hell I thought I was doing. Did I want to wreck the lathe and ruin the work? Didn't I know better than to make a big cut like that?

When on the point of offering to bet him ten bucks that he was crazier than a bedbug and I could prove it, I remembered the Chief, saw him sitting there with that quiet steady look—and I got all sugary. I had to stay on the job no matter what happened. So I said that I was sorry—I must have been thinking I was working on iron instead of steel. He calmed down, and told me not to start another cut without calling him.

Anyway I had dope, plenty of it, for my first report. Years later, I dug it out of the files and kept it as a memento of that first day.

"GT-99
"Report for June 12.
    "The train got in on time at 8:10 o'clock in the morning. Tip to porter, 25c.
    "I checked my bag in the station for 10c. The check man told me the way to get to the plant was to take a street car and I did. It took 35 minutes and I got there at just 9:00. 5c fare.
    "There were no men in sight going into plant. It starts at 7:00. The employment office had a big sign up so it was easy to see. I went in. A man said, 'Good morning' and I said the same. I told him I was a machinist looking for work and right away he said to sit down and where have you worked, etc. I told him and he asked a few questions about lathes but I saw he didn't know much about them, just asking to see if I did."

There are two pages about my conversation with the employment manager and being escorted to the machine shop. Here is the section about the lathe incident:

"I was assigned to a South Bend 16" lathe and given job T-337. This called for a spindle to be made from a soft steel forging about 6" in diameter and 3'-0" long. This is a soft steel and it cuts like butter. There are 30 lathes of various sizes but there are only enough mechanics to operate 16 of them. Eight lathes are working on the same job I have. The foreman said he still needed a dozen good men.

"The lathe hadn't been used for months and I first had to clean it up and then get a millwright to tighten the belt. He had to shorten it by taking out an inch. He used rawhide belt lacing and it took him just one hour. He is a conscientious man and claims to like his job but he knows little about millwrighting and admitted it. He was formerly a steamfitter and says that is the only part of the plant he knows much about. He could have worked faster and made a better splice if he had some of the new metallic splicers such as the Clipper. Don't think I'm plugging for them as there are three or four other makes on the market just about as good but right now I don't remember their names. The lathe ran all right when he finally got her started but it was pretty near noon. The tools were in terrible shape and I sharpened a few. This kept me busy while the millwright was working.

"Right after noon I put in a new tool and turned her in till she was cutting right up to capacity. I was taking a look around the shop at the other machines and I saw the other men looking at me kind of funny but didn't know why. Then the foreman (I don't know his name yet and haven't asked) came running up to me and said, 'What the hell do you think you're doing?' He swore a lot and cut the power and started looking at the job.

"I didn't know what he was yelling about and asked him. He said I had been taking a cut of damn near .100″ and was burning up the work and the tools too. I asked him what was wrong with that and he said she ain't good for but .050″. I saw he didn't know any better so I said that I must have made a mistake and thought I was cutting cast iron on which you can take a cut like this. He looked me over a minute or two and said that on account he was short handed he would give me another chance but that I was not to start a cut again without getting his O. K. I said I would and let her run along at .050″ the rest of the day.

"Now this bird is all wrong. Now I admit I never heard of any tables to tell a machinist how big a cut he can make on a lathe, but I swear I'm right. You have to have good sharp tools and a sort of knack of knowing just how fast and far a tool can be pushed. I was only using a feed of .080″ and these machines are good for .100″ on soft stuff like this. On a 6″ piece, you can reduce the diameter ½″ and cut .080 easy if the tool is sharp and mine was. All the other machines are doing the same job in the same slow way and this is why they are so far behind. If this bird would get wise to himself and let me bear down on her, I could make one of these spindles in an hour. They are set for 100 minutes now and I will bet I can make them in 60 minutes and keep it up all day. Now Chief I want you to tell me if I have got to stand for being called a dumb bastard like this foreman called me today. If I didn't know what I was talking about it would be

different but I will bet him or anyone else $100 cash
money that I am right and he is wrong. This shop
wouldn't be in such bad shape if there was anyone here
who knew something about these lathes. I wouldn't be
surprised if the same thing is going on all over the
place. I am using a 16″ lathe. There are four 20″ lathes
idle and four of us could be working on them and making even better time. They have got a lot of these
new type Acme automatics over on the side next to the
railroad track, and several big mills, and a lot of gear
cutters. If all this stuff is being held back by foremen
as dumb as mine, the shop is in a pretty bad way. I
wish you would look into this right away before I get
sore at this big stiff.

"This is all I got time to write tonight. There was
nothing happened when I rung out or on the way home.
This rooming house is all right for the time being. I
might move later but I paid the lady for a week ($4.00)
and will stay that long. There aren't any other roomers.
"Yours truly, GT-99."

I've written thousands of reports since, and have read
thousands written by other operators. My later ones were
more grammatical and I learned to leave out profanity, but
on the whole, this report was a good one. It told the story
clearly enough. The men in our office could readily see
that I had made an important discovery, although they undoubtedly checked up to make sure I was right. This they
could do by consulting a lathe handbook, or phoning to the
office of any machinery dealer.

A few days later the factory manager, the chief engineer,

[25]

and a couple of experts came in and recommended the maximum capacity for our lathes, and they were just as I had predicted. They also went over all the other machines in the plant with the same idea in mind. The savings which resulted were simply enormous.

CHAPTER 3

Letters from Home

G T-99 was my official designation. It had been given me by the Chief when he hired me. All the letters I wrote, the daily reports and everything else were signed that way. When the Chief, or any of his assistants, wrote to me, my real name was written on the envelope, but inside the letter started out, "Dear GT-99."

The men in the office were known by letters. The Chief was CHI. His first assistant was NY. The man who later came to open a branch office in the town where I worked was NEB. They all seemed to be the abbreviations of cities or states.

The G in my "code" meant I had been hired at the main office, the T denoted the year of my employment and 99 was my number on the accountant's books. This had all been worked out long before my time to protect us from exposure. A letter addressed to "Dear GT-99" and signed by NEB is pretty hard to identify.

Every night when I got home I sat down to write. Early I learned that if it was put off until after supper, it was twice as hard. My minimum stint was three 8½" by 11" pages, double spaced. This meant almost a thousand words. At least half the time, especially when things got to popping, there would be four, five or six pages and this meant up to two thousand words. It takes a pretty fast typist to turn out two thousand words in thirty minutes and it usually took me a good hour. I asked for more money after awhile, and the Chief doubled my pay—two bucks a day. The plant president sent him five hundred dollars to give me at Christmas as a result of the lathe episode and a few other suggestions I had made along the same line.

My landlady was a splendid woman, but she was curious about my continual typing. This was to be expected as it could be heard all over the house. She dropped a hint or two on the subject, not objecting to the noise, but with the evident hope that I would tell her the reason, and I did. This was my first job away from home, I said, and my folks were worried about me and I had promised my mother I would write to her every day. Then, and I tried to look a little embarrassed, I had a girl back home and I wrote her a letter every day, too. This was what the chief had told me to tell anyone who inquired. Later I claimed to be writing stories and trying, without much success, to sell them to magazines and newspapers. Every week or so I

[28]

would type a few paragraphs which looked like a part of a story and leave it in the machine so that anyone who came into the room during the day could see it.

I got letters from the Chief or some of his office men three or four times a week. The letters were written on the typewriter but the envelopes were always addressed in a woman's handwriting. Some of the office girls did this. For a few months after I started, each letter from the office was numbered and a little typewritten statement was attached which I had to sign and return. It stated that I had received and read the letter and had burned it.

Later, all the letters from the office had to be returned as soon as they were read. If they didn't go back by return mail, I got called for it. Still later, they passed a rule that if a man failed to return a letter he was fined five dollars and it was taken out of his pay, and there was no talking them out of it. I think some letters got lost somewhere. At all events one of us would get exposed every so often, or "turned up" as we called it, and this made the Chief mighty careful. I also had to get a post-office box. All the money I got from the office for writing reports came there every two weeks. This was sent in cash by registered mail and a receipt was enclosed for me to sign and return.

Letters from the home office to operators were written according to a set form. Invariably a letter of instructions to me would start out with some complimentary remarks about one of my recent reports. The incident might have seemed trifling to me when the report was written but the office man who commented on it would praise me to the skies. Then, there would be a gradual transition and I would suddenly find myself being called rather sharply to account for some mistake I had made in my work or for an opportunity I had neglected. After this bawling out, the letter would conclude with a cheerful paragraph or two.

"It's like this," replied the Chief when I asked him about it years later. "A good operator is as temperamental as a prima donna. I can see the reason for it, too. A man out on a job has no one to confide in and he gets lonely and sometimes disgusted, and when he is doing the best he can he resents having us send him a lot of letters which cuss him out for his mistakes. If he were right in our office, and our office men could call him in every day and give him his orders, it would be another matter and the man would take his instructions peaceably just as any other employee does. But when he's away from us it's different. He gets one letter with nothing but instructions in it, and in a few days, another of the same, and a little later another one comes along giving him hell for something. I don't blame the man if he gets to where he hates to open our letters. This caused me a lot of trouble and worry when I was starting the business and I lost a number of good men who quit because they thought they were being ridden too much. Finally I hit on the idea we use now."

In nearly all my reports I had a suggestion of some sort to make and it was fun to see how many of the suggestions were put into effect. It made a fellow feel pretty important.

It was a cinch in those days before the shops went wild about efficiency and production methods. I would have been glad of a chance to work in any shop in the country for twenty-five per cent of what I could save for my employers. The war had caused a boom in all lines of industry and there simply were not enough trained men in the land to fill the key positions. As a result, every shop did the best it could with the people it could get. Waste and loss were terrific. But what of it? The warring nations were paying high prices, and everyone was making more than he had ever dreamed of before.

But this was only part of the job, the least spectacular part. A more important feature of it had to do with personnel, what the worker thought of his job and how this might eventually affect plant operations. Each day I learned the name of another man, and this wasn't easy. You don't walk up to a fellow worker and say, "What's your name?" Such a proceeding has no place in shop ethics. You find the name on his toolbox plate, or on his locker. Sometimes you learn his clock number and look at his time card. In an office the boss takes the new employee around and makes formal introductions, but Emily Post specifies no such procedure for factory hands.

There was a tall, skinny, grouchy Southerner at a machine near me. His name, I learned from another worker, was Yancey McNeil Trowbridge. Some handicap, and no wonder he had a sour puss. My married sister lived in Mobile, and about that time she sent me a lot of the praline candy they make down there. I guess it's the favorite dish of the South, after corn licker and yams. One day at noon we were sitting in the shade eating our lunch, with Trowbridge off by himself as usual. I moseyed over his way, sat down, and handed him a big hunk of praline, saying, "They tell me all they do down your way is eat this stuff." He looked at the candy, looked at me, took a big bite and munched along for a full minute without speaking. "Man," he said, "that sure 'nuff does taste mighty fine. How'd you come by it anyway?"

The ice was broken. After work we walked down to my place together and I fed him more pralines. We had dinner and went to a movie and then to his room where he set up a jug of corn and we talked until midnight. And— I got all the dope on another man.

Needless to say, no report was written that night. Next day's report told why.

Yancey was a fine fellow, born of a good family that had come on evil days. He had gone to work and learned the trade in the railroad shops in Atlanta. Lured by high wages in the North, he had drifted up here, hating everything northern, industrial and capitalistic, and intended sticking it out only until he had saved two thousand dollars which would enable him to finish his law schooling. He was a radical in theory, or, as we later came to call his sort, a "parlor pink." His one joy in an otherwise drab world was finding an audience, one or a dozen, that would listen to his denunciation of the capitalistic system. I decided he

[32]

was harmless, and the boss agreed. In fact, he became a great bore, and I avoided him after getting his story. He was a hard worker, honest and careful—not from choice, as he hated it all—but for practical purposes. He was a queer one, who would have to be watched and possibly discharged if he began to show any signs of active radicalism, but as long as he behaved, he was an asset to the plant.

CHAPTER 4

A Cat Is Skinned

WHEN these phases of the job had been mastered, I thought my education was complete, but it merely served to pave the way for future activities with a greater scope. Almost any parrot can be taught to repeat what it hears. My real work was to direct the thoughts and actions of my fellows to conform with company policy—and make them like it. There, in one sentence, was the real reason labor spies were employed in those days.

Yet the term "Labor Spy" is not a pretty one. Big corporations even then had Directors of Public Relations; shows had press agents; wealthy men had Public Relations Counselors—but if you did the same sort of thing inside a factory itself you were a spy, a spotter, and the lowest worm on earth.

Nevertheless, we "spies," by our own reports, helped a lot of likely youngsters into better jobs. Early in my career

[34]

I started a young Italian on the way to becoming a million-aire. He would have got there anyway probably, because he had the stuff, but I gave him the first push.

Angelo spent his days with a wheelbarrow, hauling metal shavings away from the machines. He was a good-natured Guinea and we all liked him. When I was cataloging him along with the others, we got well acquainted. I was the only man in the department who spoke Italian. One day he told me of an idea he had for handling scrap. I told him to tell it to his boss. He did, using all fifty English words in his vocabulary, and his boss threatened to fire him if he ever spoke of it again. It seemed that such a system would effect economies so great that half the scrap and porter crew could be laid off—which would have been bad for his boss's ego. I studied it a little and made a report to my office, giving Angelo full credit for the suggestion. The plant snapped it up right away and put Angelo in charge at twice his salary. Two years later he quit and went into the scrap business on his own. He made a fortune in the post-war boom, and if he reads this, he will know for the first time how it all started.

Every week I got a long letter from the Chief, or one of his office men, about labor policy, wages, bonuses and things that would affect the workmen in my department, as well as in the entire plant. In conversation with the other men I had to talk this stuff up, put it all in a good light, and get the boys in a receptive mood so that when any particular plan was announced, they would be all ready for it and think it was a splendid idea. This sounds easy, but try to do it. I had a smooth line and took a lot of pride in putting things over. I wasn't one hundred per cent successful, of course, and no one could be; but if I couldn't get the men to agree with me, at least I found out just what they were crabbing about, reported it, and if the situation was serious enough the plant would make some concession—or maybe get rid of the lads who were putting up the loudest squawks. I had to watch my step and do my share of the complaining just as all workmen do; but I was careful to beef about things that didn't amount to much.

A new pay schedule was inaugurated, putting all the men on piecework. In the early days piecework rates were computed so that the average workman could make out as well as if he were working by the hour. Even so, the man who was just average got scared stiff the minute he heard about piecework. He thought he would lose out on it. When the cost department was considering changing a job from time to piecework rate, word was sent to me asking how long the operation should take. I reported what the average man could be expected to do, as well as what the better than average workman could do by stepping on the gas.

A job had come in recently requiring several hundred small shafts. Each one took a man about three hours. The job had to be set up three times, and at fifty cents an hour the labor cost was $1.50. On the first of the month it was announced that each man who worked on these shafts would receive a flat rate of $1.50 for every one he made.

[36]

We were gradually changing over to this general system and I had been trying to get the men to see the advantages in it. Rudy Bezdek, an old-school mechanic from across the water, had been working on shafts for months and he announced he was going to quit. No siree, no piecework for him.

"What you think?" he yelped. "Supposin' I get bad piece steel? Supposin' she break after two hours' work? Who's goin' pay me? No mine fault and I'm big sucker. Supposin' no stock like last week and I'm doing nothing half day? By gosh, I'm workin' here three years, but I'm quittin' now and goin' good shop."

The old man was a good worker and I had put him down as being one hundred per cent for the shop, but here he was walking off the job—and we needed him badly. I trailed him out to the locker room, got him in a corner and urged him to try the new rates for a few days; but he couldn't see it.

"Listen, Rudy," I said in desperation, "you're as good a workman as there is in the shop, aren't you?" He agreed. "Well, I'm a good man too, and I've been making shafts for a couple of weeks, turning out the same number you have, and I know damn' well I can turn out a lot more than I've been doing. Now I want you to stick with me for a week at this new rate. I'll promise to pay you anything you lose and I'll pay it right out of my own pocket. My rate is $31.50 a week, the same as yours. And I know for a fact that I can make at least six more shafts this week than I did last week—if I really work at it—and I know you can too. Don't think I want you to stick because I like you. You're a pain in the neck, but you're the oldest guy here. If I set the pace all alone and bust the rate wide open, the gang will be sore as hell. How about it, grandpa? Wanta play ball or be a quitter?"

This got him sore at me, and he forgot to be mad at the shop and the cost department. He finally agreed, and we went back to work. That night the old geezer showed me his card. He had made one shaft every two hours all day long, five in all, or nearly two more than usual and had earned $7.50 instead of $5.00. And he hadn't worked himself to death either. You couldn't speed up the machine in cases like this, but we made speed by better planning and by changing our set-ups. He had beaten me, and in fact, I never was able to catch him on this particular job. From this time on every job had to be piecework or he yelled to high heaven. He just about took care of this part of the work for me. Whenever I heard of a man crabbing about a fair piece rate, all I had to do was sick Rudy on him and he got in line.

During the fall a big new plant was opening on a certain date. The chief at once informed me that I might expect it to offer higher wages than our plant was paying. Sure enough, when the opening day was announced in the papers our whole plant rang with gossip. Following the Chief's advice, I watched the leaders and best workmen to see if any of them were planning to leave.

Walking home, I broached the subject to Johnny Miller,

a man with three brothers and four kids in the plant. Johnny was the champion bowler of the city and swung a lot of weight. Yes, he was laying off shortly to give the new place the once-over and he might make a change. No, there was nothing wrong with his present job, but the new shop was closer to his home and he could save thirty minutes a day on the street-cars. Yes, his boys would probably go with him, and, if he liked it, the whole bowling team might come over. In other words, if Johnny took his amiable, good-natured self to the new place he would probably lead a procession of some two dozen of the best men in the plant. I talked as well as I could about the fine way we had been treated, how wages had steadily advanced, and how much of a blow it would be to have the bowling team leave us.

Johnny said that I could get a job at the new place too. He suggested that I come with him in the morning. We had a couple of beers, and then a couple more, but he was dead stubborn as a mule, and I couldn't bring up a single argument that would change him. We then talked of other things and it finally occurred to me that bowling was the big joy of Johnny's life and if he could be reached along that line, I might get somewhere.

Quite a while before, it had been arranged that in cases of great emergency, I could call the plant president and put him hep to anything of importance. I decided it was essential to keep Johnny's gang in the plant. Bear in mind that this was in the days prior to America's entering the war,

[39]

and that there was a labor shortage. I called the president on his private line and told him the story, suggesting that if a little consideration could be shown the bowling team, it might help. He was quick and knew his business. "All right, 99," he said, "just leave it to me."

He sent a uniform salesman around to see Johnny the next day to say the boss had decided to present the bowling team with new uniforms for the coming season and what men were on the team and when could they come down and get measured? If you followed bowling in those days, you saw the big write-ups Johnny and his gang got that next winter at the Bowling Congress.

There is more than one way to skin a cat.

CHAPTER 5

I Am Promoted

THE plant was to close down for the Christmas week-end and the Chief instructed me to come to the main office for a conference. This was my first visit since I had been employed almost six months ago, although the Chief and two of the office men had passed through my town several times and had discussed things with me. Business must have been improving. They now occupied a whole suite of offices and I was taken around and introduced to the entire force, stenographers and all.

The Chief informed me that I had worked myself out of a job, and he instructed me to discontinue at the end of the month. For the first time I learned that there were three other operators in the plant, and we had all been working along the same general lines. One was a stock chaser, one a millwright, and one in the porter crew. For several months it had been apparent from my reports that conditions in the machine shop were excellent. The change in the wage scale had been made without much friction and this, it seemed, was the principal purpose for which I had been employed. The porter was to quit at the same time while the other two would remain to insure against trouble cropping up unexpectedly. The Chief just grinned when I asked the identity of the other operators; so I never asked such a question again.

"Now, 99," the Chief said, with the same serious look I had come to know so well, "I have another job for you and you start on it as soon as you've gone back and arranged to quit the one you have now. In a few days you will receive a letter from the town where your next job is to be. It will seem to come from an old friend of yours, and he will tell you about the plant where he is employed and suggest that you come to work there. He will hold out hopes that you will get a foreman's job in a short time and paint such a rosy picture that you would be a fool if you didn't take the next train. I am arranging to have this letter written and you can show it to your friends and your foreman. Of course you will be sorry to leave as you have had fine treatment there, but workmen are always moving around like this and it's not unusual. The big thing is for you to leave in such a manner that you can always go back again and they will be glad to see you. If you have any outstanding bills pay them all up and tell the people you are leaving and why. Who knows? It may be that a year from now, or twenty years from now, you will be back there again and you want to be all set to pick things up where you left off."

Then, the Chief took me into a little office and turned me over to the man who would direct my new activities. He was a former operator who had been advanced to the office, but he confided to me that he would like to be back in the field again. His code was BUF, and of course he was called that in all correspondence, and even in conversation.

My new assignment was pretty well "down East." It was a fine old industrial town where some of the best machinery in America was made. The plant in which I was to work made all of the parts that went into its particular product. In this respect it differed from plants that buy parts from various manufacturers and merely assemble the finished article. This plant had a pattern shop, foundry, machine shop, a crew of toolmakers, a large assembly floor and a complete engineering department. There were some six hundred employees and most of them were highly skilled. It was said that the place was nearly a hundred years old, and when I saw the men coming to work the morning I arrived, I felt sure that a good many of them had been in the plant from the day it opened.

BUF explained that a union organizer had spent several months in the city a year ago, and had succeeded in forming a local union including most of the machinists in this plant and quite a few from other shops. At first the owners had scoffed at the possibility of trouble from this source. Then, a committee from the union had waited on the president of the company, and although no important demands had been made, and there had been no suggestion of a strike or violence, it was quite evident that the request for a few minor changes in working conditions was backed by all the power of the local, and the president had deemed it wise to acquiesce. After this he had sent for the Chief pronto, and had arranged to have an operator assigned who could find out what was going on and give advance warning of future demands, as well as direct union affairs in such a manner as to conform, if possible, with plant policy.

I was the ambassador selected. This was a promotion, since the manipulation of union activities was generally entrusted only to men of experience and judgment. I learned later that no such man was immediately available; so I was taken from my other job and pressed into service on this one.

BUF and I talked about the new job for the next two days, and then I returned to my original assignment.

CHAPTER 6

Hail and Farewell

THE day I received the letter the Chief had mentioned, I dropped around to call on a millwright named Muzik with whom I had become quite friendly. Each time he appeared in the machine shop I endeavored to talk with him for a few minutes as he was a mine of information about what was going on in other parts of the plant. With a little judicious questioning I generally got an item or two for my reports. He was a good-natured chap, about my own age, a fast worker, and well liked by all of the machinists.

Every factory has several millwrights who work directly under the superintendent, their job being to keep the machinery and equipment in running order. (A machinist or a machine hand is responsible only for the actual running of the machine as it manufactures a product.) Millwrights repair or replace belting, move machinery, align shafting, babbitt bearings, tear down machines for repair and reassemble them, erect pipe lines, and sometimes even do the electrical work.

Muzik roomed in a house near my own. When I arrived, his landlady called him to the top of the stairs. I told him I'd dropped in for a chat as I was leaving the job in a few days and wanted to say good-by. He asked me to come up. Instead of waiting for me at the top of the steps, he ducked back into his room and I could hear him scurrying around at a great rate. I took my time going up and when I reached his door he came out to greet me.

We talked for a few minutes about my new job, and he agreed that it was a fine opportunity. The conversation then turned to the shop, and we talked about the new gear cutters that the millwrights were installing in a newly built addition to the plant. Then we got to talking about our experiences in other shops, and a very pleasant hour was passed.

I kept changing my position to see different parts of the room and finally discovered what I had been seeking. Pretending to choke on some tobacco from my cigarette, I asked Muzik where I could get a glass of water. There was a lavatory off one end of his room, and, as I had expected, he got up to get the water for me.

As soon as he reached the lavatory, I went quickly over to his bureau, which was about six feet away, and took a book from the top. The volume was a machinist's handbook. Sticking out from one end of it were several sheets of blue paper. I unfolded them and read: "28 Dec. 19—. Dear GN-42:" . . .

Before I had a chance to read any of the letter, Muzik came back with the glass of water. When he saw the papers in my hand, he became livid. He set the glass on the table and moved towards me. To forestall anything in the way of violence, I rose to my feet and said, "Put her there, 42, I'm GT-99 and I'm mighty glad to meet you."

He was dumbfounded, but after a few seconds he stuck out his hand. We had a good laugh and then sat down to talk things over in earnest. I told him of the slip the Chief had made, admitting that there were other operators in the plant. Analyzing the millwright crew, all of whom I knew, I had decided by the simple process of elimination that Muzik was my man.

I had deliberately called on Muzik that evening at the time he would probably be writing his report. His scurry back to his room when I was announced had confirmed my suspicions. I had been hoping to find a way to bring the subject into our conversation but had not been successful. Then I had looked around the room hoping to see something of a suspicious nature, and finally had noticed those slips of blue paper. The letters I had received from our office were on paper of the same peculiar shade.

We agreed that no one at our office should be informed of my discovery. It was considered very dangerous for operators to know about each other when on the same job. The rule against it was one of the most rigidly enforced in the business. I suspect the reason was to prevent two operators from getting jealous of each other, or quarreling, and one of them deciding to turn the other up.

We talked until long after midnight. I told him everything I could about my department that might help him after I was gone, and he was glad to get the information. We also chatted about the Chief and the other members of the organization with whom we were acquainted.

This was the third job on which he had worked and he had learned a lot of little tricks that were new to me. For instance, he told me it was never wise to announce in a report that you were starting out to procure a certain piece of information that might take several days. If you were not successful in getting the facts, you had a hard time explaining it to the office. It was better to wait until the matter was finished and then report it in detail. This made you a hero if you had succeeded and if your efforts fell flat, the matter need not be mentioned at all.

Muzik was also a great believer in always having a juicy bit of information saved up for a rainy day. Every so often, a day would come along when nothing of a reportable nature occurred. The office men were always querulous when we made such a report. They simply couldn't understand how you could be in the same plant with a thousand other workers and not get a big story every single day. Muzik's plan was to hold out several items, suggestions for improving efficiency as a rule, and use them to pad out otherwise dull reports.

"I learned the trick last year in Toledo," Muzik said. "I was millwrighting in one of the big furnaces there. For five straight days I was all alone inside of a blast furnace replacing air pipes. I went into the furnace at seven in the morning and came out for half an hour at lunch time. I saw some of the men at noon, but I was so deaf from the hammering they were doing on the outside of the furnace, I couldn't hear a word. I spent the afternoon alone inside the furnace again and when I came out at night, we all went right home. All I had for my reports for five days was the time I started and stopped and one statement, 'I spent the entire day working in the furnace all alone and didn't see anyone or talk to anyone.' They were going to fire me, but the Chief stepped in and saved my job."

Muzik expressed regret that we had not gotten together sooner because we might have been a great help to each other. After I left town we corresponded up to the time he left to join the Army. He did not return to our company after the war and I never heard of him again.

My friends in the plant were genuinely sorry to have me leave. Their sincerity was so apparent that I stayed until the following Sunday to attend the party they staged for me at the Sokol hall. This was directed by my old friend Rudy Bezdek and some of his countrymen, and it was a howling success in more ways than one. Unlimited beer was on tap, and since I was a member of the plant glee club, and a pretty fair banjo player, all the singers turned out and we sang until dawn.

I remember singing "My Buddy," which was at the height of his popularity. I put a lot of pathos into it, and when I got through old Rudy put his arm around me and started to weep. I suspect he had surrounded at least a gallon of beer by that time. He addressed the crowd: "Boys, I want to tell you about this feller here. He is my buddy and the best one I got. I'm goin' quit last summer when starts all this piecework business. And what does mine buddy here? He gets me so mad I stay in the shop just to show I can turn out more work than him. And what happens? What happens? I ask you. Here's what happens. I'm makin' more money today like I never saw before. I'm coming here from old country twenty-three years. I don't like this America. I'm saving my money for go back to old country and live with my peoples. Then what happens? Everybody crazy and fightin' and killin'. I say, 'Rudy, you in helluva fix now. Can't go back old country. Don't like this America. Whatsa use?'

"Here's whatsa use. My buddy here, he come say, 'Rudy, you good man. You stick along mit me. We make plenty money. You don't stick, you a quitter.' I'm damn' mad but I stick and now next week I'm taking out first papers and I'm going to stay in America. Buddy, good luck. Goodby, but sometime I see you again for sure. You want my house, my money, my wife, anyt'ing I got, she's yours anytime."

The foreman had been invited, and he came for a little while, but left early, not wanting to put a damper on the party. He was man enough to get me aside and tell me he had been all wrong the day he bawled me out about the lathe incident and it was a wonder he hadn't been fired when they made the shop survey a little later. He hadn't connected me with the affair at all. He wished me good luck and promised me a job if I ever came back.

I had purchased a second-hand car with the bonus the company president had given me. The sun was just coming up when I got into it and started east for my next experience. I had the feeling of leaving a job well done and recall thinking what a fine world it was and what a fine lot of people there were in it.

CHAPTER 7

I Join a Union

Getting a job at my new location was almost as difficult as the last one had been easy. There was no employment department. An assistant superintendent did all
the hiring. I sold myself to him without much trouble and
he admitted there were a few openings in the machine shop.
New England conservatism was the order of the day, however, and I must produce references. This was a new
wrinkle; I had never needed them before. A whole week
went by before I was able to get the "characters" and secure
another interview. It resulted in my being employed and
told to report the following morning. This deliberate method
of doing business impressed me, and I did not forget it.

The machinery this plant turned out was all custom-
made. There was no such thing as a standard article. As
soon as an order had been placed the job was designed in
the engineering department, patterns were made, castings

poured and machined, and the steel sections worked up in the machine shop. The finished parts were then assembled on the erecting floor and the machine was tried out. Then it was taken apart and shipped to the customer, where it was reassembled and put into use. The larger machines weighed close to one hundred tons, and, as they operated with precision approaching that of a watch, a high degree of manufacturing skill was needed.

This skill was in the heads and hands of the machine-shop employees and these were the boys who had joined the union almost one hundred per cent. If they decided to strike, the plant would be tied up just as effectively as if the entire force walked out. More than half of the employees were in this department.

Shortly after I started to work I was given the job of turning out racks and pinions. They were to be of a grade and fineness I had heard of but never before attempted. I was honestly afraid I wouldn't be able to hold up my end as a workman. My hat is off to the bunch of bogtrotters with whom I worked for the next year. If I ever have a plant of my own and need real machinists, I know where to get them. The best ones would be only about one hundred and twenty years old now.

BUF, my supervisor, told me to report along efficiency and production lines and forget the union for a little while. At the end of the second week, however, I was walking home alone, when I heard someone calling me from behind. It was a big fellow named McBride, a kind of gang leader on the erecting floor, who had already helped me several times with mechanical problems. In most plants the erecting crew were not machinists, but here they were the best ones in the shop, as they had to make adjustments and repairs if the job didn't assemble as it should.

McBride was with two of his crew whom I didn't know. I joined them, and they asked me to stop in with them for a glass of beer.

"This is Bill Greenlief from the tool room and Tom Eggelston from my gang on the floor," said Mac when we were comfortably leaning against the bar and had given our orders. "We are all members of the machinists' union here in town. You've been in the plant a couple of weeks and we hope you'll stay. So we decided it would be a good idea to tell you about the local and see if you wouldn't like to join. Most of the men in the plant are members, and there are quite a few from other shops in the neighborhood. We have initiation every month and we're trying to get a big bunch to join the night of the annual banquet on Washington's birthday. I'm chairman of the membership committee and Bill and Tom, here, are on the committee with me. We've looked you over and we don't mind saying we'd like to have you with us."

Mac blurted this out with sincerity but showed evident relief when he had finished.

"No, boys," I said slowly and thoughtfully, "I don't think I'm much of a prospect. I have known a good many men who joined unions. They all tell me things go along fine until there is a strike and then they always lose out. They lose their jobs, their savings are used up, and they never get anything in the way of advantages to make up for it. If I have to belong to the union to work here, I think I'll pack up and move along somewhere else. There are lots of good jobs in open shops. I've never been able to see that a union was much good."

This was said with as much finality as I could muster. The words were really BUF's who had predicted I would get such an invitation sooner or later. Of course I wanted to join, but if I had to be begged and wheedled into joining, it might help to avert suspicion in the future.

Greenlief turned out to be the best salesman of the group. He called my attention to the insurance benefits, and explained them carefully. He also produced a magazine published by the union, and called my attention to several instructive articles in it. I hesitated, far from convinced.

"Wouldn't you like to walk down to our meeting rooms?" asked Eggleston. "Some of the men usually drop in there after work. We've just bought a new pool table and there are some tables for cards. No gambling, you understand," he was quick to add, as I looked horror-stricken; "the house rules don't allow it, but it's a nice place to loaf, and particularly for a single man in a strange town."

So we adjourned to the union hall. The president, a man named Snider, was the center of a chatting group and I was introduced all around. Most of the crowd were from my plant, and Snider was one of our toolmakers, a fine man with a simple, direct approach. Everyone liked him and it was not hard to understand why he had been made the chief executive of the lodge.

He left the men with whom he had been talking and joined us while we made a tour of the rooms. Snider got in some good arguments in favor of joining, stressing the advantages of being better acquainted with one's fellow workers. He belittled the matter of a strike, and assured me there was nothing he could think of that would make him leave the plant. He had been there twenty-seven years.

Finally I gave in and signed an application. This pleased the boys a lot since it gave them an even dozen to initiate on the night of the first annual dinner. The international organizer, a man named Reynolds, who had started the lodge, was coming all the way from Montreal for the occasion and they were anxious to show him how they had been carrying on since he had left them to their own resources.

The initiation into a labor union is similar to that of any fraternal order. There is a little rough stuff, such as riding the goat, or its equivalent, and then the candidate recites the obligation to the lodge. Being "obligated" is the expression. All the unions I ever joined, and I've joined several, have a lot of fine sentiment embodied in the ritual; I think that the members who take it seriously should become pretty good citizens.

The guest of honor, Reynolds, was a silent but interested spectator during the initiation and he had plenty of reason to feel proud of the officers, as everything went off without a hitch.

There were five candidates from my plant, and the rest were from other shops in town. All of us had to do stunts. I played my banjo and sang a few songs. "When You Wore a Tulip" was a big number in those days and I got quite a few encores.

The banquet was one of those long-drawn-out affairs. All the officers had to make speeches, the visiting organizer had to make a speech, and then darned if they didn't call on every last one of the twelve initiates to make a few remarks. I was the last one, and those of the audience who remained were pretty nearly asleep. This was my first union speech and I probably never had to talk under worse conditions. I told a funny story, and then another, and then another. The first woke them up, the second got a laugh, and the third had them yelling.

This was all the Chief's doing. It had been his custom, from the time I started on the first job, to send me one or two funny stories each week. It was a theory of his that a funny story is a mighty fine entering wedge in any situation. One of the reasons for my popularity at the old plant was that I always had something funny to tell, and the men got to expecting it. I told some of the Chief's best ones that night, and ended up with some platitudes on the general subject of fraternal organizations. BUF had prepared the latter for me in case I had to talk.

The organizer came to me as soon as the show was over, asked for my name and I saw that he made a note of it. I was now a union member and, finally, a full-fledged labor spy.

CHAPTER 8

For the Good of the Order

THE machinists' union met on the first Tuesday of each month. Nothing in the wide world, so far as I have discovered, is so boring as the average union session for the transaction of business and the initiation of new members. The third Tuesday of each month, we held a smoker or social gathering. It's hard to tell which was worse, business meeting or smoker. There was seldom any business on which to act—a few bills to pay, a lot of committee reports of no consequence, and talks on "the good of the order" by anyone who desired to make them. The smokers would have about thirty men, but there was seldom much more than a quorum at the business sessions. And after a while, the attendance at the social gatherings began to dwindle away. (I had been appointed chairman of the entertainment committee.) This was all very satisfactory to me; and BUF and the Chief were plotting a way for me to give the local a final push into oblivion. Then something happened.

I had been advised earlier by BUF that there was a machinists' strike in a town about two hundred miles away. The men had been out for a month. The Chief had been called in to help settle it. My plant shipped the "struck" shop quite a few machine parts, and we were working on a good-sized order right at the time. Strike-breakers had been imported and there was a good deal of violence. The union seemed to be losing ground, so the international officers, who always manage a strike of any importance, decided to start working on the companies who supplied equipment or raw material to the shop where the strike was in effect. In due time, our local got a letter instructing us to bring the matter to the attention of all shops within our territory who were supplying anything of this sort.

I was faced with the very situation I had been hired to prevent, and what was I to do? In later years, when such emergencies arose, I acted by instinct, just as an experienced automobile driver shifts gears. But in this emergency the Chief and BUF did nearly all the planning, while I did the leg work, and later the voice work.

The man who had organized the lodge, Reynolds, still had general advisory jurisdiction over its activities and the striking plant was also in his territory. He had spent all of his time with the strikers since they walked out, and he was trying to negotiate a union agreement with the plant owners. Every day the union had a mass meeting at which

Reynolds made a speech and tried to prevent defections from the ranks of the strikers. As I have come to know strikes, if they are not won by the men within the first week, they are apt to be lost entirely, or a face-saving compromise is worked out which is almost as bad as a defeat. This strike had got to the point where the union was ready to accept even such a compromise. It was a last-ditch stand that had made them ask for sympathetic strikes in plants such as ours.

Our grievance committee, which had been merely a name in the past, took official cognizance of the matter. The committeemen went around with an air of mystery and concern, indicating that the cares of the universe rested on their shoulders. In a few days one of them got scared and asked to be relieved; so the president appointed me in his place.

The six members of the committee, plus the president and walking delegate, met the day I was appointed. A letter had come from organizer Reynolds begging for some action on our part. After a lengthy discussion, we prepared a letter for submission to our company, in which the whole situation was reviewed and a formal demand made that no more merchandise be shipped to the "struck" plant so long as the strike continued. It was assumed that we would go on strike if the demand was not complied with. I had kept silent most of the time, but when we were about to adjourn, with the matter settled, I spoke up.

"Boys," I said, "as a newcomer in union affairs I have kept quiet, but I have been a most attentive listener. The

[61]

letter you have prepared is a fine, straightforward appeal for fair treatment in accordance with American ideals and customs. I am heartily in favor of sending it so that our employers will know we are united with our brothers in making a demand for simple justice.

"But there is one thing I am in doubt about. It occurs to me that we are taking a good deal for granted regarding this strike situation in the other plant. All we actually know about it is the information contained in a few letters and circulars we have received from Brother Reynolds. He is a mighty fine man, and I am proud to be numbered among his friends, but after all we have ourselves to look out for and I feel we should go a little slow on this. I think we should be certain of our ground before we get the lodge to approve this letter. I am a single man, and if we had a strike here, and lost it, all I would have to do would be to move on to another town and get another job. Most of the brothers of our lodge have families and homes and have lived here all their lives. If we should lose out is Brother Reynolds going to continue the payments on these homes, and buy food and clothing for the children? There is just a little under two thousand dollars in our treasury and that won't support us very long after our wages stop."

There was a murmur of approval from the other committee members. I continued, "Here is what I propose: Let us lay the letter on the table for the time being. We will have to get the approval of the lodge at a regular meeting before we send it anyway and that will not be for two weeks. In the meantime, I will be glad to lay off on a Saturday and drive over to visit the strikers with Brother Snider and a couple of the others on this committee. We will talk with the officers and some of the strikers and get this story at first hand. If we do that, we'll be able to tell our lodge just what is going on, and what events led up to the strike; and we won't be in so much danger of making a mistake."

They fell for it, good old conservative heads that they were, and a date was made to go on the coming week-end. As soon as BUF got my report on this meeting, he okayed the inspection trip and hastened to confer with our client. As a result, it was arranged that the factory manager should send Snider, the president of the local, out of town on the following Friday to supervise a repair job in the plant of a customer in the opposite direction from the strike. This looked like a routine matter and the committee accepted it as a piece of bad luck. I flatly refused to visit the strikers unless Snider was with us, and that put the trip off until the following week-end. This delay gave the strikers time in which to lose even more ground, and made the picture we finally saw seem considerably blacker.

I now know that my inspiration for this inspection trip marked the turning point in my career. If I had merely listened to the proceedings of the grievance committee meeting and reported it, I might have received instructions from the office to do something of the sort, but it would very likely

have been too late. In any event I would not have been criticized. Only one labor spy in a hundred ever rises above the
rank of the ordinary shop workman who makes his routine
daily shop report, year after year, as assignments come
and go.

CHAPTER 9

A Friendly Visit

THE following Saturday, at 3:00 A. M., we started in my car, and got to our destination at noon. This was pretty nearly a record for the cars of those days. We arrived at the hall that the strikers were using for their rallies while the meeting was being addressed by the walking delegate who had active charge of the details of the strike. It was easy to see that the strikers were sick and tired of the way things were going. It was the kind of atmosphere I came to understand better later on. With just a few words from the right man, the crowd could have been induced to throw up the sponge right then and there, or, on the other hand, be goaded into an attack on the plant.

"Men and brothers," shouted Reynolds, interrupting himself in the midst of his business agent's talk, "I have a surprise for you that will prove unionism is just what I have been preaching. In the rear of the hall I see four brothers from another lodge who have come to pledge their support. Brother Snider, bring your delegation right up here to the platform. I want these loyal men to see you and hear your message. Brothers, this is real unionism and a glorious demonstration of it. I wrote to Brother Snider's lodge along with other lodges whose members work in plants which supply either raw material or finished products to the firm which has treated you so disgracefully. I explained the situation you are facing, and asked them to insist that none of the plants in which our brothers are employed ship anything to your plant until our rights are recognized and our agreement signed. Here, brothers, is the answer. Brother Snider, the president of the lodge, has come in person at the head of a committee to assure you of his support and I will now call on him to address the meeting and give you his message. I introduce Brother Roscoe Snider, president of local 1009."

This put Snider on the spot and he had to produce. He wasn't much of a speaker, and he had a hard time trying to live up to the introduction he had received—and still not promise anything. In the meantime, Reynolds had cornered me at the back of the platform and asked what we had come for.

"Well, it's like this," I said. "We prepared a letter demanding that shipments stop, and it will be presented to the membership for approval next Tuesday night at the regular meeting. In the meantime, we just decided to take a run over to see you and learn how the strike was coming along so we could make a better report."

By this time, Snider was getting his talk pretty well mixed up and Reynolds asked me if I would say a few words. I agreed, so he cut right in on Snider and introduced me. Nobody minded, Snider least of all.

I started out by making them laugh and then gave them a little "baloney" about the beauty of American ideals as exemplified by our union, and ended up with the prediction that they would win, as "right is mighty and must prevail." This was like holding out straws to drowning men. I hadn't said a single constructive or concrete thing but they seemed cheered up a little and most of them had laughed for the first time in several weeks. The other members of our committee were not called on to speak, and in a few minutes the meeting broke up after a final appeal by Reynolds to maintain the picket line for "help is on the way." Picket lines, by the way, are no recent invention, but existed at least fifty years ago.

Reynolds and the other officers kept us with them the rest of the day, and all we saw and heard was to the effect that the strike was as good as won. With some help from us and a few other union plants, the thing would end up with a smashing victory, we were told. We had no chance to talk with the rank and file and when we went to bed that night I called this to the attention of my crowd. We decided to go out to the vicinity of the shop in the morning.

The Chief had told me just where to go. He had operators among the strikers, and it was easy for him to get the layout. I pretended to drive around aimlessly but finally stopped in front of a little grocery store and said I would get a few smokes. Snider went in with me. We started to talk to the storekeeper about the strike, and while we were at it a man came in to buy some groceries. The storekeeper shook his head and said something we couldn't hear. The man started to wave his arms and wail about his hungry children and his wife who was ill. All the proprietor did was lead him to the door and tell him to go to the union for the strike benefits they had promised.

"That's the worst of this thing," said the proprietor when he returned to us. "That man is as good a workman as there is in town. He has a nice little house down the street with a wife and three kids. He used to make good money and was paying for his home. When the strike started, he had good credit with me and all the other stores around here. We carried him for a while but now he owes me nearly forty dollars, and even if the strike is settled tomorrow and he goes back to work, it will take him months to pay his debts. I'd hate to tell you how much I stand to lose on account of extending credit to these people. I hear the mortgage company is going to take his house, and there are hundreds of others in the same fix."

I asked if he thought the strike was lost.

"Sure it's lost," was the reply. "It started nearly three months ago, and at the end of the first week the company had hired enough men to keep going, and new ones are coming every day. I know a couple of the foremen and they tell me the new crew are turning out just as good stuff as the old one. This strike started on a Monday. The shop pays on Saturday night and all the men had a week's pay on hand. When the first Saturday came around and the boys had no pay envelopes to take home to the missus, they started to hear plenty around the house, and that doesn't help any. They've had twelve straight Saturdays with no pay, and the situation is desperate in a good many homes. Most of the single men have gone away to find other jobs; but the married ones can't dig up enough money to move."

When Snider and I returned to my car, two men were standing beside it talking to the other members of our committee. We heard some of this conversation which was just about the same as we had heard in the store. Later I learned that one of these men was an operator the Chief had planted there to work on us. He did a bang-up job, but the other fellow was just as good and he was a real striker. The first man to approach the car was begging a dime to get some milk for his kids. The other (the operator) asked how conditions were in our home state. He had noticed the out-of-state license on the car and was on the point of leaving town in search of work. In his opinion the strike was lost. He had borrowed enough to send his wife to her people (so he said) and, with all of his savings gone, he was going to hit the road in search of a place to make a new start. The operator was particularly bitter against Reynolds and the whole union system. I asked him for the story of the strike and he gave it to us.

The union, he said, had been started six years ago as the result of a wage controversy, and the company had finally signed a union agreement. This had been renewed every two years and everyone had been happy. The shop had not been strictly "closed" as it was not obligatory to have a union card to work there, but some eighty per cent of the workers were union members and the company recognized the union as the bargaining agency that represented the employees.

This year when the time came for the new agreement the union demanded a completely closed shop, which meant that all employees must have a union card. There had been no controversy about wages or hours or conditions, simply this one point, and the company would not concede it. The union had voted for the strike after being talked into it by Reynolds and a couple of hot-heads, so our informant said, and the men had been out in the cold ever since. A few had gone back to work and a lot of others would have liked to but were afraid of being beaten by the strikers.

This all made a profound impression on my crowd. We spent the rest of the morning calling around and by noon had a score of tales of the same sort. In fact, the story told us by the Chief's operator was the simple truth and right in line with the others we heard.

I got the committee to slip out of town without going to the hall again, or looking up Reynolds or any of the other officers. On the way home the silence was so thick you could have cut it with a knife and I knew the men were all having a good hard think. I didn't disturb them either. They were all family men and right at that moment their homes and jobs looked pretty good.

CHAPTER 10

End of a Union

THE next night, Monday, the grievance committee met. The purpose was to talk over the letter we had drafted, in which we made demands on the company, and get it in shape to present to the Tuesday lodge meeting for approval. One of the men who had made the trip didn't show up that night, or the next night either. He was cured of unions.

We looked over the letter and talked a little while in a disinterested sort of way. The members who had not made the trip were told about it. These men were typical old-school working-class men. They were native born, had served their time in our plant or in one of the similar shops nearby. Their ancestors had settled the town in colonial days. The thought of having to move, or not being permitted to work in the plant any longer, literally made them ill.

Finally Snider said, "I was talking this over with the wife last night and again this morning and we decided it

[71]

would be better to go a little slow. In fact, I just about made up my mind to resign as president. I'm in favor of helping out those strikers, but somehow I don't think I'm the man to have charge of it. I told Adams [the vice president] about it today and offered to turn the job over to him. He and I are good friends but when I told him about our trip yesterday, he wouldn't have anything to do with it. I don't quite know what to say as this is something I ain't used to."

The oldest man on the committee, Albert Brainer, then had his say: "Boys, I wasn't with you yesterday, but I heard about what you saw and heard. If I hold my job until next fall, I will have been with the company just fifty years. For the past twenty-two years, no machine has gone out of this plant without my final O.K. on the elevating mechanism, and not once in all that time has there been a complaint from a customer. After fifty years, I am entitled to a pension. I am going to get that pension next fall and move back upstate where I was born and go fishing every day in the summer and sit around the fire in the winter. No union or no union officer is going to take that away from me. When this union started, we were told it was a sort of club where we would have a little beer to drink and maybe play cards. I am quitting the union right now and I am going to tell all my friends to do the same thing." The old man put on his hat and stalked out.

We talked the thing over from all angles again. I never saw a group of men so sick of anything in my life. We decided to ask the rest of our local to back us up in refusing to have anything whatsoever to do with the strike, and this gave me the chance I was waiting for.

"Men," I said, "turning this thing down isn't going to settle it. As soon as we do that, we'll have Reynolds up here on our necks and there will be hell to pay. I'm one of the newest members and I don't like to get up in meeting and suggest anything but—well, Snider wants to quit as president and I don't think we will be able to find anyone else who is anxious to meet old man Reynolds when he comes up here with blood in his eye after we turn him down. I believe if we tell the boys tomorrow night about what we saw and did yesterday, and tell them how Brainer, and some of the rest feel, they'll decide that there's only one thing to do, and it's this: Let's roll up the charter and ship it and all our books and everything connected with the local right back to the international offices. Let's bust up the whole show and scatter the pieces so far they'll never be found."

Well, that settled it. They were all for it. I had voiced the sentiment of every man there. For a while we talked about who was to bring the thing up at the meeting. Each man hated to be the first one to quit publicly. Finally it was wished on me, and after a good deal of argument I took the assignment.

I framed up an excuse to stay at home the following morning, and called BUF for advice on how to present the story.

"Put it on a high moral plane," he said. "Quote the Bible, quote the Constitution of the United States. Quote Washington and Lincoln. Call me again at noon and I'll give you some more dope." We had only about ten hours, and in an emergency such as this long-distance tolls were the last thing to worry about. The client paid them anyway.

When I called again, the Chief answered. He gave me the outline of a speech that was a corker. It was based on the theme of avoiding foreign entanglements, which he had lifted from Washington's farewell address.

A speech of this sort would have made little impression on a group of coal miners, or packing house employees, or similar groups in which a large percentage are foreign-born, but with these one-hundred-per-cent Americans, it made a bull's eye. There were eight votes against winding up the affairs of the lodge, and over a hundred for it. The news had gone around that something big was on the way and this meeting of the local had the largest attendance in its history. Snider and all the other officers were as pleased as Punch, and I kept right after them until we got the charter, books, seal, and everything else boxed up and shipped back to the international headquarters.

Reynolds arrived on the jump three days later and there was a grand lodge vice president with him. They ran all over town for a few days and then gave us up as a bad job. They couldn't find a single man who would tell them just what had happened. The minutes of the last meeting contained only one sentence: "The lodge decided by a vote of 109 to 8 to go out of business and it is so ordered." This was signed by all members who had voted for the motion in regular round robin style. Reynolds heard I had made the speech of the evening and came to see me, greatly disappointed because he had hoped I would become an active worker. No, I said, I had been scared out with all the rest of the committee by what we had seen on our inspection trip. I was so sincere that he put me down as an honest, if misguided, youth; and I don't think he suspected me at all.

But he was in for an even greater misfortune. While he was trying to mend his fences in our town one of the Chief's men at the "struck" shop made a grandstand play and ended the strike. This was the last of Reynolds. He lost his job as organizer and went back to his trade.

My work was finished, but I stayed on awhile in case there should be any smoldering embers of the union. I remained until fall and had a splendid time. I think every former union member looked on me as a boon to the community, and Snider particularly couldn't do enough to show his appreciation. The plant shut down as usual for two weeks in August and I hung around town to see if the men would get to talking unionism during their idle hours. I didn't hear the word the entire time, although I went fishing with some of them nearly every day.

A few days before Thanksgiving BUF dropped in for a talk. I went over the entire situation and he seemed satisfied. He then told me that this particular assignment was ended, but that another was awaiting me. Once more I spread the word to my shop friends that I had been offered a better job elsewhere. Inside of a week, I had wound up my affairs and was on the way.

CHAPTER 11

"Over There"—and Back

M Y NEW job never materialized. That was the spring
America declared war, and I told the Chief I was going
to enlist. He had just returned from Washington, where
he went each month to confer with government officials on
the subjects of sabotage, alien enemies, etc. He told me all
information gleaned from our reports on this subject was
turned over to a government department which investigated
it further. Our operators had already done a good job of
ferreting out enemy sympathizers and saboteurs who were
doing all they could to delay our war preparations.

"I have just the place for you," said the Chief. "Both the
military and civilian branches of the War Department need
all the good investigators they can get. With your knowledge
of foreign languages they will take you in a minute, and I
shouldn't be surprised if you made a big success. It will
also keep you in practice for our work when the war is over."

But I turned it down. I still felt that I was a better mechanic than a spy and when a chance came along to get into the Ordnance Department, I took it. After six months in this country I went to France with a lieutenant's commission and spent a year with a combat division repairing machine guns and the famous French 75's. To my mind the French field artillery is the finest mechanism I ever worked on—and considering the great variety of machines with which my job of labor spy brought me into contact my opinion should mean something.

During the post-Armistice doldrums, when we were all speculating wildly on what might happen next, I was ordered back to the States and told to report to the Ordnance Department in Washington. Taking the first available ship, I returned to the capital, presented my orders, and was directed to the desk of a certain Captain who was vaguely reported as being in the G-2, or intelligence section of the general staff. Arriving there, the first person I encountered was BUF, wearing a captain's uniform. When we had told each other about our war experiences, I asked him where I could find Captain Martin. It turned out that I'd been talking to him all along. I had forgotten his name as a result of all that BUF business.

He told me that the Chief had been serving as a dollar-a-year man, and was about to resume his business operations with more business than he could handle. He had arranged my recall, and within a few hours I was out of the Army and on the way to our old headquarters. The Chief appeared in a few days, and within a week BUF and several other old timers returned.

The Chief's work in Washington had kept him in close touch with working conditions throughout the nation. He told us that there had been a great change in all forms of employment. Common labor was getting forty cents an hour and up. Skilled craftsmen were making nearly one hundred dollars a week, and no plant could get enough help in the open market at any price. There was a great shortage of everything. Factories which had been turning out nothing but war supplies for eighteen months were now trying to catch up with their normal business. They were licked from the start. They could get neither material nor man-power in sufficient quantity. Labor discontent was rife. The IWW was spreading terror throughout the West, while other radical groups of unknown origin and objective were disrupting the Middle West and East.

The Chief was so short of experienced operators that he was accepting orders only from groups of manufacturers, and placing men in their communities where they would mingle with the workingmen at large and endeavor to keep informed of the general situation. This was what he had in mind for me, and I started for Centerville, a middle western city of a quarter million inhabitants, as soon as I had joined a union. It seemed best that I arrive on my new job with a "card in good standing." One of our men was corresponding secretary of the electrical workers' union in a near-by town and he fixed it up for me. The secretary also wrote my card out so as to indicate that I had been a member for several years.

When a member of one local union moves to another town, he "deposits" his card with the local into whose jurisdiction he has moved. The secretary of the local receiving the card then writes to the local which issued it to inquire about the visitor's record. When a favorable reply is received, he "demits," or joins the new lodge. He is then entitled to all the rights and privileges of a regular member except that he usually is not eligible for elective office for a year. If a letter were written about me my friend the secretary would be the one to answer it. My knowledge of electricity was limited but it was not intended that I should work at the trade. Every lodge has members who have not followed the trade for years, but who retain their membership because they like the crowd.

Centerville, my new home, had been founded, so the monolith in the public square announced, in the early years of the nineteenth century. A hundred years later it had become an industrial center of national renown. The descendants of the first settlers were bankers and prominent attorneys. The first manufacturing plants had been attracted by land grants from the city fathers but other factories had come later because of a plentiful and docile labor supply and convenient transportation. After the war, the more progressive manufacturers had become worried about the heretofore ideal labor situation, and had called the Chief in.

After I got established at the headquarters of my union, the next thing was to get a "cover," or visible means of support, to explain my presence in the city. Employment in a shop would restrict my activity. It was, therefore, necessary to find work that would allow me to come and go as I pleased. It had long been my ambition to try my hand at selling, and this seemed a good chance. If I could find an article of particular salability to working men and women, so much the better.

I soon learned that there was a great housing shortage and that a number of low-priced land developments were starting up in the suburbs. After a little investigation I made a deal with one of these companies to sell both lots and houses on a straight commission basis. This meant I was paid only for what I did, but at least I would have a regular occupation. When necessary, I explained my failure to work at the electrical trade by saying that my war experiences made it advisable for me to stay in the open as much as possible.

This was an ideal set-up. I had a lot of business cards printed, and roamed about the city trying to sell real estate. The best part was that I sold a lot of property, and made more on commissions than I could possibly have made working in a shop. My salary from the Chief was now two hundred and fifty dollars a month, with an expense allowance of one hundred dollars additional. After I got the hang of things in the real-estate field I made three hundred dollars a month or better in commissions for eight straight months. Things tapered off with the coming of cold weather but, like the ant, I had laid up my winter food and could exist on it until warm weather returned. This was what I told my

[80]

friends when winter arrived and it gave me an excuse for spending a few months in comparative idleness.

The labor situation in town so far as AFL (American Federation of Labor) unions were concerned was quiet. What had made the employers jumpy was the continual stream of wild-cat organizers from the Lord knew where. They were on soap boxes along the main street every night, and in the neighborhood of the larger plant gates each day at noon. This was in the months preceding the great steel strike. I learned that a good many of these gentry were in some manner connected with Foster and the gang of quasi-Communists who were endeavoring to get this major disturbance under way. Others were merely opportunists who had been forced to keep quiet during the war and were now at large, advocating sweeping reforms of every sort, before every audience they could get. Most of them were ineffective and harmless, but their actions were enough to cause unrest in any community.

CHAPTER 12

Jerry on the Job

THE most intensive organizing effort of the summer took place in a suburb of Centerville, called Northtown. This community had been built up around several huge factories manufacturing the same product. There were some eight thousand men living within a small radius, and all were engaged in practically the same kind of work. The factory owners had "improved" some extra land they owned by building several thousand small frame houses on it, and selling them to their workers. This meant that the workers were pretty well tied down, and a permanent labor supply was assured. Furthermore, the employees of the plant belonged to no trade for which there was an existing union. Where such a situation exists, it is a fairly safe bet that wages and working conditions are not so favorable to labor as in the larger cities where a workman can quit his job if he doesn't like it and get another in a day or so.

[82]

I became aware of the presence of organizers in this suburb in June, and tracked them down without much trouble. They had rented a vacant store, and a sign painter had just finished erecting a banner announcing the headquarters of the "Northtown Employees' Mutual Benefit Association." Inside I could see tables piled high with literature. On entering, I was invited to help myself. A smooth-talking young man asked if I worked in town and I told him I did. He immediately made an effort to sell me a membership in the association. It promised a number of recreational facilities such as playgrounds for children, athletic teams for adults, an insurance feature along assessment lines, and a prospective building and loan plan.

"You are a newcomer," said my informant, probably noticing my war service button. "These companies here have a long record of poor pay and bad working conditions. The employees have never had any organization which would stick up for them. And who knows? Possibly our Mutual Benefit Association will be the one to lead the way to better wages and conditions. We have pretty close to one thousand members right now, and when we have two thousand we will be in a position to start our program."

"Are you affiliated with any of the labor organizations?" I asked.

"None whatsoever," he replied emphatically. "One of our people, Mr. Risko, was an organizer for the boot-and-shoe workers a number of years ago, but he saw the fallacy of the AFL multiple-union idea and resigned. We believe it is wrong to take the workingman's dollar to support a lot of highly paid officials in idleness." From his point of view the situation at Northtown was what we came to call a "natural" in later years—a town with upwards of eight thousand people, its wage-earners underpaid, overworked, and subject to post-war unrest.

I sensed that this crew of organizers was "phony" but couldn't put my finger on anything definite. I hung around for a couple of days and talked to dozens of employees, and found a number who admitted membership in the association. They spoke optimistically of the promises they had been given.

It seemed that most of the recruiting was done in the worker's homes at night by a crew of solicitors. I confirmed this and found there were a dozen men working on a commission basis. The first payment on the initiation fee was two dollars. The salesman retained a dollar, and turned the other in to the office. Some of them must have been making ten dollars a day or more.

I found a few employees who had been told that they might expect the association to lead the way to higher pay, while others had been told nothing of the sort. I also found a few members who had been told that the plant officials were sponsoring the move. It was plain that the salesman were thinking only of their commissions and stopping at nothing to make sales. In any event, the organization was growing by leaps and bounds.

A conference took place between the Chief and the owners of the group of plants in this vicinity. It resulted in a plan of action that was new to me but had been followed successfully by the Chief under similar conditions. It was, the Chief told me, simply to start a counter organization and steal the show.

Within a week, the Chief phoned me to meet him in a city fifty miles away. When I arrived, he introduced me to a man named Jerry McVey, of whom I had heard. He had been with the Chief for several years and was the senior union operator in our company. The Chief asked me to tell Jerry all I knew of the Northtown situation.

"Can you work it, Jerry?" asked the Chief when I had finished, and Jerry had asked me a lot of questions about the layout of the town, nationality of the people, location of meeting halls, vacant lots, etc.

"Chief, I can knock that job off inside ten days," Jerry said with finality. "All I want is 99 and one other man to help me."

"Boys," said the Chief, getting out of his chair and walking around the room in his excitement, "this is one of the greatest opportunities we ever had. We're just breaking into this town, and this state. I'm as sure as I'm alive that you two are going to make history here, and you're going to make it in such a way that these manufacturers won't be able to forget it. I predict that when you get through with this bunch of yokels [meaning the employees who were being talked into joining a union] they won't let a union organizer into the town as long as they live. The very mention of the word 'union' is going to be like a red flag to a bull. I was a little afraid there wouldn't be much activity down there, and the clients might decide to lay 99 off in a few months, but this will cinch his job for life.

"I want you boys to trust each other all along the line," he said, taking us both by the arm. "Jerry has been with me since the week I started in business and I'd trust him with everything I have. And 99, [for some reason I never quite understood the boss always called me 99, even when we were alone] I don't mind saying you are the most promising youngster on the list. You'll learn a lot from working with Jerry. Ask him questions, argue with him and make him tell you why he does everything. He knows all I know about this business, and I want him to pass it on to you. I want you to move along the way Jerry has and work your way up in the labor movement. This is the time to start. Inside of two weeks, you are going to know a lot more about how it's done."

I went back to my job, the Chief returned to his office, and Jerry departed on some mysterious mission of his own. The informality of the whole thing struck me with something akin to horror. Three men in a smoky hotel room, making plans that would leave a lasting mark on the lives of thousands—and all part of the day's work. Perfectly calm, entirely impersonal, just as a crew of woodchoppers would start cutting in a forest. Two weeks and we'd have all the timber down. It had taken a century of uninterrupted growth; but a man with an axe could stop it forever in a few minutes.

CHAPTER 13

We Organize a Union

ONE of Jerry's principal assets was a "pipe line" to the main office of the American Federation of Labor, where he seemed to be well known and liked. He had been active in union circles for some twenty years and knew many of the big labor leaders. His job with us was to keep in touch with these people and get as much advance information as possible regarding national union trends and plans.

He showed us a letter from an international union official thanking him for favors recently done for the labor movement. The letter ended up with a highly complimentary paragraph asking Jerry to continue "the good work," and practically giving him authority to go anywhere in the country and organize where and how he desired.

A week after I first met him Jerry came to Centerville on a trumped-up pretext. I was present when he met a few of the biggest labor shots (without my help) and became righteously indignant when he heard of the freelance organizing going on in Northtown. (He was also introduced to me, as we were not supposed to have known each other heretofore.)

"Gentlemen," he addressed us emphatically, "this is indeed a grievous situation and one which merits immediate action on the part of organized labor. We are faced with the spectacle of thousands of brother workers, crying for union organization and leadership, while we stand idly by and permit a pied piper to lure them on to destruction with empty promises and puerile patter. I know that you gentlemen are busy with your own affairs or this unhappy situation would be corrected at once. It happens that my business is of an unusual character, and occasionally affords opportunities for me to engage in labor activities, which are my greatest joy. I have had experiences as an organizer with several of our international unions and if you gentlemen are willing, and will approve my application to the American Federation of Labor, I will wire at once for permission to organize a Federal labor union to answer the crying need of these men." This did not sound like a common workman speaking, but there are some powerful spellbinders in the labor movement, and McVey was one of the best.

(Note to capitalists: The exact function of such bodies as Federal labor unions is defined in the glossary.)

It seemed that Jerry had arranged to have his request for authority to organize a Federal local in Northtown granted by the AFL since I had last seen him. Nowadays, such a request would be granted, but someone would come out from headquarters to keep an eye on things.

Jerry's application was approved by the AFL at once, and he went into action. In the meantime, the employers had arranged to make things as unpleasant as possible for the mutual-benefiters. The landlord was "requested" to make them vacate their offices and no others could be found in town. They were forced to move their quarters over a mile away, to the edge of Centerville.

Jerry, on the other hand, was given a free rein. His first move was an automobile parade through the main streets of Northtown, with banners announcing a mass meeting in the high-school auditorium that night.

The procession moved slowly. Jerry sat in the rear seat of the first machine, a big touring car with the top down. He wore a black sombrero, wing collar, bow tie, Prince Albert coat and a white vest. He looked a good deal like the proprietor of a medicine show, and, as a matter of fact, he had been just that before he joined the Chief. He'd got hold of one of those old Gabriel horns they used to have in some cars in those days. He had a fellow in the front seat who played it every little while, and of course you could hear it all over town. There was only one tune appropriate to the occasion, and he played it—"There'll be a Hot Time in the Old Town Tonight." After the show Jerry asked me if there was anything he had missed. "Yes," I said, "you forgot to have a man riding ahead of the procession in a horse and buggy saying, 'Hold your horses, folks, the elephants are a-coming.' " He said he was sorry about having overlooked that.

"Friends and fellow citizens," Jerry began in his best camp meeting style when the procession reached the school house, "I thank you for coming. It has been said in the Scriptures that 'many are called but few are chosen.' So it is tonight. The entire city was called or invited, but only this few have chosen to respond. I am glad the number is so small. With a small group, we can gather around the fireside and converse as friends are wont to do. This is as it should be. You know nothing of me. I know a great deal about you. I have a message you will be glad to hear. Lest any be under a misapprehension, my sole purpose tonight is to give you a message. I have been selected by the American Federation of Labor, that great voluntary association of working brothers, to come to your town and tell you the true and beautiful story of organized labor in the United States."

As I had to go in and act as a sort of usher, I didn't hear the rest of his talk; but I could hear him whooping it up for a few minutes longer. He then invited the crowd to come inside. Some of them tried to sit in the rear of the auditorium but Jerry made us bring them up front.

About two hundred people were there and he gave them a rip-snorting talk on straight unionism. He tore into the Mutual Benefit Association, challenged its officers to a debate, cast aspersions on the character of the organizers, dared them to give an accounting of their funds, and made the welkin ring for a solid hour. The press had been invited and, as news was scarce, Jerry and his speech made the front page of both morning papers. He did not say a word about organizing. He merely told what was wrong with the Mutual Benefit and pointed out the advantages of a real labor union.

The following morning he opened an office on the main street and sat there all day talking to anyone who came in and handing out literature.

The second night he had another parade and ended up at the ball park, as he thought the high school would be too small. He was right. At least two thousand people came, and he gave them much the same speech. He had invited all our labor friends from Centerville, and sprinkled them through the audience. They shouted and clapped every time he made a good point. The applause helped a lot and I never heard so good a speech. I thought I was pretty fair in small gatherings but I had never had a chance to perform in a place like this, and I learned a lot just listening to him. He introduced the foremost laborite of Centerville, who endorsed Jerry officially, and then a few telegrams of congratulation from various labor leaders were read, which made things seem even more authentic. Jerry invited everyone to come back the following night, and closed the meeting by having me lead them in singing "America."

As I had plenty of time on my hands, I volunteered to

assist him and my offer was accepted. I spent my days in the new union office, or driving Jerry around in my car. Never have I seen a man work harder, or gain friends faster than he did. Within four days, he was "Jerry" to most of the town. He himself had a phenomenal memory for names. For first names, at any rate, as he seldom called a man by anything else.

The fourth day after Jerry's arrival was Sunday. He had a little secret meeting at noon to which he invited one or two prominent employees from each of the shops. I later found he had carefully picked men who did not know each other. He told them that the time was ripe to launch the organization, and he invited them to petition the American Federation of Labor to issue a charter for a Federal local. (Jerry had authority from the AFL to "organize" but the application for a charter must be made by local men, who would be the founders.) He wanted no office or salary for himself, but would stay with them in an advisory capacity until they got started and then go on about his business. He predicted they could get several thousand members in a week.

They fell for it and signed the petition that he drew up right before them. Then they elected temporary officers to serve until the charter was received. Jerry maneuvered the thing so that every man had an office except one. Then someone remembered that they had forgotten to elect a treasurer. The last man got the job. Jerry suggested that they open the books for membership applications at the meeting that afternoon, and that each application should be accompanied with a payment of two dollars to show good faith. I was not at the secret meeting but Jerry told me the details afterwards, realizing that I might have to handle such a show myself sometime.

The afternoon meeting was a sell-out. Most of North-town was there and a lot of people were turned away. Jerry only talked twenty minutes, and ended up with a rousing invitation to join the organization that had just been founded. The charter members were introduced from the platform and, from the applause they received, it was evident that Jerry had made a wise choice. Each of the founders was placed at a desk where lines formed, and the cash and applications started to roll in.

In about two hours, we took in $3700. This meant 1850 members and I wouldn't be surprised if this was a record for union recruiting, until the CIO appeared eighteen years later. All the next day, women were coming to the office to enter applications for their husbands, sons and brothers. We heard that there had been a small riot at the Mutual Benefit office, where several hundred disgruntled members had vainly demanded a refund of their money.

On the eighth day after Jerry's arrival, he told me that there were seven thousand applications on file. This meant about $14,000—less a very little he had used for printing, etc. That night at the meeting he had the treasurer read a financial report, and this made all the members feel good. A flying squadron was organized to keep after those few employees who had not yet joined.

I can't remember seeing so much enthusiasm over anything in my life.

CHAPTER 14

"Union Field"

AT NOON on the tenth day, Jerry and I were in the organizing office, checking over the list of applications for membership. Suddenly the president of our new local came in on the dead run. Taking several books from the pockets of his coat, he waved them about wildly.

"He's short!" he shouted. "He's short a thousand dollars. He's a crook. Get him! Find him! Have him arrested!" and a lot more of the same. Jerry calmed him a little. The books he was waving were the record books of the union treasurer.

"Where does this guy work?" Jerry asked, putting on his hat and squaring his shoulders. He looked much the same as Wild Bill Hickok must have looked when he started out to get the "varmits" who had held up the Deadwood coach. His get-up was about the same.

[95]

"I was there and he didn't come in to work today," wailed the president.

"This is no time for fooling," said Jerry with finality. "We'll swear out a warrant and have him arrested." I agreed to drive them to town in my car. It was necessary to go to Centerville, as Northtown was only a village, and the law enforcement facilities in it were pretty sketchy. We got the warrant in jig time, and two deputies accompanied us back to Northtown.

We went to the house where the treasurer roomed. The landlady said he had gone out the night before, and had not returned. He kept his room locked, and she had not gone in. We broke down the door. All his clothing and other belongings were gone. He had skipped out clean as a whistle.

The bank reported that the account, amounting to almost $14,000, had been closed out the afternoon before. Two names were required on every check, that of the president and the treasurer. The president admitted that the treasurer had been keeping a blank check in his possession with the president's signature on it. When petty cash was needed around the office, the treasurer could add his own signature to this check, fill in the amount needed, and get the money from the bank without delay. This was the check the absconder had used, and, as it was all in order, the bank had not questioned him when he drew out every dollar.

That night there was a meeting. The poor old president appeared broken-hearted, and boo-hooed all over the platform. Jerry told the crowd to have faith in the police; he was sure the criminal would be caught, and the money all recovered.

Up to now I had visualized nothing more than a union under our control. Now I began to smell a rat. If the union's money was not recovered, the lodge would never survive the blow. If this happened, it might safely be deduced that unionism would be a dead letter in Northtown for a long time to come. This had been our mission and it now seemed to be accomplished. Jerry had promised to complete the job in ten days. This was the tenth day.

Another thing: Jerry had asked the Chief for two assistants, me and one other. I had never seen the other. Why hadn't he appeared? GT-99 was being left out of something. Where was McVey anyway? I found him at the union office talking to the officers of the lodge, but he finally finished, and I took him home in my car.

"Jerry," I asked when we were alone, "who is this treasurer guy anyway?"

"For all I know, he was a painter who worked in the little shop near the power house," said Jerry sadly. "The sheriff and the lodge officers haven't discovered it yet, but he'd worked there less than two weeks. I hardly know him at all, and hadn't laid eyes on him since the fall of 1915, when he helped me break up a strike in a paper mill up above Albany. The Chief wired me an hour ago to say steel common had gone up quite a little today and he thought it was safe to buy some. If he had said it was *un*safe, it would mean that our late treasurer missed the boat which is taking him to Rio for a little vacation.

"The high spot," he went on, as if talking to himself, "was making the shortage so evident that even this dumb president could find it. That makes him a hero, and I'm just an innocent bystander—which is all I want to be."

I complained about having been kept in the dark, but Jerry calmed me by saying, "Here's something to remember, 99—the fewer people there are who know *all* your business, the less chance there is of a slip. Our treasurer didn't know it all. Our client didn't know it all, or anywhere near all. Even the Chief didn't know quite all of it; and I'll admit there were a couple times when I wasn't quite sure as to whether I knew all about it myself.

"That honest, surprised look on your pan when you heard of the theft was worth a fortune. If you had been in on the know, you *might* have looked that way—and then again you might not. It was best to have you in the dark with all the rest.

"We're not out of the woods yet. I feel pretty certain I'll be arrested and maybe held for investigation. It's possible they will pick up all the union officials and give them the once over. Our clients have passed the word down for the sheriff not to spend too much time on the thing, but it will be necessary to go through the motions anyway."

"But how about the cash?" I asked. "Does this treasurer get to keep it? After all, it belongs to the men who contributed it."

"The answer to that," said Jerry with every element of satisfaction in his voice, "is one more proof that the Chief is the greatest guy in the world. He almost turned this job down, for he knew the employees of the entire village were treated like dogs, and he really thought they were right in demanding better conditions. Before he took the job, the Chief extracted a written promise from his clients that they would use the men's money plus an equal amount from their own pockets, to give these people all the things our union and the poor old Mutual Benefiters were promising."

All of us were called before the county prosecutor for questioning. The investigation made a bigger stir than the organizing drive, and the poor people who had turned over their hard-earned money were the laughingstock of the entire state. Nothing came of the investigation, of course; and Northtown citizens did their best to forget about the whole episode as quickly as possible.

A fine big athletic field and clubhouse were started at once by the manufacturers. They named it "Union Field." They explained that this was to symbolize the "union" of interest between the different plants of the suburb, as well as "union" of thought between employer and employee.

CHAPTER 15

How to Form a Union

"14 July 19—.
"Dear GT-99:
  "Now that the situation in the suburb of Northtown is quieting down, it behooves you to work out a plan whereby you will shortly become a delegate to the Central Labor Union of Centerville. By 'shortly' I mean *within a month*.

  "You have made good progress in meeting the labor leaders of your city but you are no closer to becoming a member of the CLU than the day you arrived.

  "As it would probably be impossible for you to oust the CLU delegate from your own electrical workers' union—at least quickly enough to do any good—there is only one alternative and that is for you to organize a local of your own and get yourself elected as delegate to the Central Labor Union from the local you organize. I will leave the working out of the details of this plan to you but it must be gotten under way at once.

  "I know there is a lot of organizing going on in the shops and factories of your town. We have got to find

[100]

out where this is and let our clients know so they can get rid of these union men as fast as they join. You did a good job in getting on top of the Northtown affair as soon as you did but you were simply lucky. You can learn a little here and there about union activity without being a member of the CLU, but the only way you are going to hear all about it is by becoming an active member of the central body.

"My orders to you are to drop everything else until you solve this problem.

> "Very truly yours,
> "CHI."

This letter arrived a few days after Jerry McVey left town at the conclusion of the Northtown incident. It was as strong a letter as the Chief ever wrote me, and I appreciated the gravity of the situation.

The Central Labor Union in our town was composed of representatives from thirty-eight local unions. Most of these were in the building trades; carpenters, plumbers, bricklayers, plasterers, electricians, steamfitters, hoisting engineers, iron workers, painters, roofers, glaziers, cement finishers, and workers of all the other crafts that had anything to do with the construction work. The other trades were barbers, teamsters, streetcar men, cigar makers, printers, railway clerks, musicians, and a very few of the shop crafts including molders, machinists, pattern makers, blacksmiths, and garment workers. As in most large cities, the building trades ran the Central Labor Union show. They had more crafts represented and their locals were the largest. The delegate from the plumbers' lodge was president of the CLU and all the rest of the officers were building tradesmen.

In the days of which I speak, the building trades were better organized all over the country than any other group. They worked for different contractors as jobs came up and there was almost no such thing as continual work with the same employer. When a contractor had no building contracts on hand his entire force consisted of a few clerks, his superintendents, and a few foremen.

If a contractor secured contracts for several buildings he might need to hire several hundred men immediately. If he were to have advertised and examined the applicants himself it would have taken him forever. He knew it was much more practical for him to call the headquarters of the various unions and ask for, say, thirty laborers, eight bricklayers, five carpenters, three iron workers, and whatever else he needed. If he wanted them all to report at eight o'clock the next morning they would be there, and he would get as good men as there were in the market.

The building trades were seldom subjected to the attentions of the labor spy. A single contractor was seldom concerned enough about the labor problem on any one job to go to the expense of hiring us. The electrical local to which I belonged was composed almost entirely of men who worked for electrical contractors, wiring buildings, and installing lighting fixtures. They went from job to job, and employer to employer as needed.

On my present assignment it made little difference to

which local I belonged, so long as I became the delegate to the Central Labor Union, and thus became friendly with the leaders of all unions and gained their confidence to such an extent that they would tell me what was going on in their various trades. The officers of a well-organized local union let the rank and file know as little as possible about what was going on. The leaders of every enterprise do the planning long before they make any public announcement. Labor unions operate in the same manner. The president of the photo-engravers' union might spend several months laying plans for a strike, and none of his members would suspect it. Meanwhile he might discuss the matter every day with some of his CLU buddies, who had no connection with his trade, but who knew strike technique.

The delegate of the CLU from the electrical workers' lodge was the business agent. He had held the position for a number of years, was popular with the members and there was no chance for me to replace him. The annual election had taken place in February, shortly after I demitted. He had been re-elected for another year, so that was that.

I would have to form my own union—but what one? (Fortunately this would not necessitate my resigning from the electrical workers'; it was not unusual for a man to belong to more than one union.)

In the public library I found a government pamphlet which listed all the labor unions in the country, with their membership, location of headquarters, and something of their "jurisdiction." There were plenty of unions with no local in

Centerville but I couldn't very well start a lodge of glass blowers when there was no glass factory within hundreds of miles. Neither could an inland city have a longshoremen's local, or an organization of lumberjacks. I was stuck. For a couple of days all I did was chew my nails and pray for inspiration.

By this time I was well established in the real-estate business and knew a good many of the real-estate brokers and salesmen, as well as their office help. My best friends among this crowd knew of my union connection and kidded me a good deal about it. On the afternoon of the second day a young lady clerk in the real-estate department of a bank remarked that the heat was killing her, and that if she belonged to a union, she would strike for cooler weather. I left her office with a broad grin. She had given me the tip I needed.

Within twenty-four hours a letter was on the way to the headquarters of the clerks' international union saying I could organize a lodge for them, and asking for the procedure to follow. Three days later I got a big package of application blanks, record books, instructions, and everything else I needed.

In the meantime I had not been idle but had lined up twelve of my friends who thought it would be a great lark to become real union members.

Within ten days I had the charter and we completed the organization by electing officers, and you may be sure that GT-99 was the delegate to the Central Labor Union.

[104]

〰〜

CHAPTER 16

〜〰

Moving Up

THE CLU met on alternate Thursdays. When the next meeting night arrived, I was at the hall bright and early with my credentials. This event caused a big stir. It had been twelve years since the last local had been founded in the city—with the exception of the Northtown fiasco, of course. The old labor leaders not only welcomed me into the fold; but I also got kidded a good deal, and was asked a thousand times if I were sure the treasurer hadn't skipped out with the money.

The president made a nice little speech announcing the admission of the clerks' local to full membership. When he had finished, an old chap named Clancy rose and said, "Brothers, I have been chairman of the organizing committee for three years. I'm getting old, and I'd like to retire. I want to resign my job of chairman, with the understanding that our new brother will be appointed in my place. He has proved there is a lot of good union material in town, and if he will lead us we can go right out and get it."

"Brothers," I said as soon as the applause died down, "this expression of confidence is more appreciated than anything I have ever encountered in my life. It is true that I have been fortunate in directing the formation of a new local to further the cause of organized labor in our city, but I am not yet ready to shoulder the responsibilities our kind brother has proposed. You will recall my efforts and the efforts of all of us in Northtown a few weeks ago. This was a mortifying experience and when it was over, I took the lesson to heart and made a solemn promise that I would proceed at once to make up for this mistake, and not rest until I had given our community a new union to take the place of the one which was so completely wrecked by an unscrupulous renegade. All I have done, brothers, is to fulfill my promise. I seek no other reward than to work in the ranks and I insist that the brother who has just spoken shall retain his office.

"Should the time ever come," I added as an afterthought, "when there is a vacancy on the organizing committee, I will be glad to try to fill it should you still think I am qualified."

There were five on the organizing committee and they fell all over one another in an effort to resign in my favor.

Thus, inside of three weeks, I was not only in the CLU, but a member of the most important committee from my point of view.

"What can we do to stimulate interest in the union movement?" was the question asked by chairman Clancy at the first meeting of the committee that I attended. No one had anything constructive to say. After giving all the boys a chance to answer, I spoke.

"Labor unions have been suffering from the same complaint as all other fraternal organizations," I said. "Most of the members have been to war. They dropped their cards, and haven't got around to renewing them. Today our men are too busy getting back to civil life to think of anything other than jobs and homes and families. I have an idea which will capitalize on this very thing and serve as a recruiting ground for all the locals in town. The American Legion is chartering posts rapidly and I think there are enough union veterans in town to organize one. We will restrict it mostly to union men but of course we can take in non-union people. When we get them in, we will see that they join the union of their craft. I'm sure I can line up at least fifty men within a few weeks and we can get a charter. I suggest calling it the 'Union Post' of the American Legion."

The committee approved my suggestion unanimously. They had been counting on me for a new idea and here it was. At the next CLU meeting I announced the program, and asked the delegates if they would like to have the organizing committee, or those members of it who were eligible to Legion membership, visit their locals and talk about the subject at one of their regular meetings. This was left to the individual lodges, but within a week I had received invita-

LABOR SPY

tions to come to twenty of them. I was the only member
of the organizing committee eligible for Legion membership;
so it was seldom that any of the rest went with me, and I
suspect they were just as glad to get out of it.

Visiting most of the locals in town could have only one
result as far as I was concerned. Whether I got any recruits for the Legion or not, I became acquainted with
every lodge president and business agent, as well as most
of the other officers. I not only met them, but, as I was the
only active member of the CLU organizing committee they
had seen in years, it was only natural for them to ask my
advice regarding their own organizing problems. And could
I give it? Well, not very well, of course, until I knew just
what they were doing along that line at present.

For example: the stationary engineers asked me as a
special favor to stay after the meeting I attended at their
lodge, and sit in at a conference of their own organizing
committee. They were really working hard for new members, and were all excited about getting applications from
the two engineers employed at the Riverview Hospital, one
at the stove works, and three in the big agricultural imple-
ment plant. While they were talking, I glanced idly over
the six applications they had laid on the table.

A few minutes later I excused myself to go to the wash-
room, where I wrote down the names of the applicants for
future reference. Both the stove plant and the harvester
company were clients, and the president of the former concern was a director of the hospital and as bitter an anti-

union man as ever lived. All these names went in with my report and within a week six engineers were looking for jobs after having been fired so quickly they didn't know what hit them.

There was a time back in the early days when I used to worry about the men who were fired after I had reported on their union connections. Finally I talked to Jerry McVey about it and the answer he gave me seemed so sensible at the time that I didn't bother about it again for a good many years.

"The bosses are bosses," said Jerry, in his usual emphatic manner. "As long as this is the case, they are not going to give in to any unions unless they have to. That's why they hire us. Supposing somebody comes along and starts to organize a shop. We report a few men for joining and they get fired. The organizing stops and the rest of the men keep on working.

"Now supposing the whole shop joined up without the boss knowing it. When he finds out about it, he's apt to fire them all, isn't he? Which is worse? To have a few men canned, or to have the whole shop fired? Or, supposin' he doesn't fire them when the shop gets organized, and they pull a strike. Well, the whole shop is out a couple of months, and loses all that pay, and then probably loses the strike to boot. Isn't it better to have a dozen guys fired when we report them, and save the jobs of all the rest? It's hard on the guys who get fired, I suppose, but they'll know better next time."

Another use for such information as I had secured at the meeting of the stationary engineers was to have one of our salesman, or the Chief himself, call at the plant where the men were being organized and sell the officials on the idea of employing a full time operator who would keep in close touch with the employees and report what was going on. When I was able to dig up exact information on which to work, it wasn't hard to scare an employer into giving us a job. I was given a little bonus by the Chief every time he got a new job as a result of my efforts.

I was instrumental in getting eleven men placed in various shops and factories within the next few months. We had the town pretty well covered. As time went on, some of these operators joined the unions of their craft, and worked from within the organization. The American Army was nearly demobilized by now, and it was easier to get operators to work in the shops.

One of the problems of a labor spy is to keep from doing any active organizing himself. Occasionally I would have to step out and get a few members, but they would be musicians, or truck drivers, or such—men whose jobs weren't in the key industries. Once I got caught out on a limb and had to take applications from three molders, but I saw to it that they were fired within a month and blacklisted at every shop in town.

Within a few weeks after I started to visit local unions to talk about the American Legion, the post was chartered. As I was the principal founder, it was natural for the boys to elect me the first commander, and I served for two terms. Just as the president of the CLU was the labor spokesman for the city, I became the veterans' spokesman. In a short time I was being put on civic committees of all kinds, and had more invitations to speak at banquets and meetings than I could possibly accept, in view of my union duties, which of course came first.

That fall I addressed the Chamber of Commerce, the Rotary Club, the City Club, the Woman's City Club, a flock of churches, the parent-teacher association, and the students and faculty of the local college.

CHAPTER 17

Who Hires Labor Spies?

THE Chief made several trips to Centerville while I was
working my way up in the labor movement. We discussed all the plants that contributed to the support of my
contract, and he explained the particular requirements of
each one. I had expected to find the larger places on the
list, but I was amazed at the number of shops with less than
fifty people. And for the first time I learned the identity
of all the firms who engaged the Chief to send operators into
their factories. Why a little factory making optical supplies
and employing only thirty men would have an undercover
operator for eight straight years was a mystery to me, and
I asked the Chief about it.

"That's easy," he replied. "Did you ever see the bunch
that works there?"

"Yes," I said, "and they were the finest collection of
squareheads I ever saw."

"That's the answer," replied the Chief. "They are a bunch of squareheads and worth their weight in gold. Did you ever try to hire a man who is a real expert in the manufacture of lenses and other kinds of optical supplies, such as binoculars and telescopes? Well, I don't envy you if you ever have the job. This shop has about thirty employees, and every one of them is a highly skilled mechanic from the old country. They all came over here before the war. Hardly any such mechanics have arrived since the war. Almost no one learns the trade here, so the supply is diminishing. The older ones drop out of the picture, and there aren't enough young ones to replace them and take care of the normal increase in the business. Every company that hires men of this type knows it must treat them like kings, or they will get temperamental and walk off the job. If they do this, the shop simply can't replace them unless it hires men of the same type from other companies in the same line. All the companies are in the same fix, and every once in a while some of the unethical ones try to steal men from their competitors.

"This is the reason for keeping our man. They've paid me ten dollars a day for the eight years he's been there, but they've made a profit on him at that. Twice during the eight years, agents from competing plants came here and tried to hire as many men as they could get to come to work for them. Our old operator reported it immediately and our client was able to balk the deal."

That got me thinking. "Well, is there any business that *doesn't* use labor spies?" I asked.

"No," the Chief replied. "Every employer in the world uses them to some extent. Suppose a man opened a shop to make paint. I can picture him calling on a customer, getting an order, and returning to the little factory where he ground his colors, mixed them with oil, put the finished article in a can or barrel, and delivered it. It was a one-man show and the boss did it all. As time went on, his business prospered and he hired a man to work for him. The new man learned the business. They sold more and more paint, and finally the owner hired a second man. The second man learned the business, and he too became an asset to the firm.

"One fine day the owner called the first man to one side and said, 'Bob, how's our new man doing? Does he like the job? Do you think he wants to stay here? Do you think he might go to any of our competitors and try to sell them the formula we worked out for that new blue paint? I'm counting on you, Bob, to let me know what's going on when I'm not here. I'm going to give you a little raise just to watch these things for me.'

"Has our paint manufacturer employed a labor spy?" the Chief asked. "Is there an employer in the world who doesn't resort to this practice whenever he desires? Is it within the rights of an employer to do this? If it is within the rights of an employer to engage one of his own people to report on what his other employees are thinking and doing, doesn't he have the same right to call in a firm of experts to do the same thing?

"Take a large plant with several foremen. Does a foreman

have a right to make a deal on the side with one of his trusted
men to let him know what the rest of the crew are thinking
and doing when his back is turned? I'm referring to employers and foremen who are fine, upright men, but who
believe it is a good idea to know as much about their departments as they possibly can. By 'right,' I refer to the moral,
or ethical, side of the subject. The legal side is another
problem.

"I said that every employer in the world employed spies,
but I've spoken only of the manufacturing industries. If a
housewife employs a maid to do housework, is the lady to be
condemned if she searches the maid's room occasionally to
see if there is anything there she should know about? Has
she a right to sit up late on Thursday night to get a look at
the fellow who brings the maid home on her day off? Is
there an office manager in the land who doesn't have a means
of determining just what his people are thinking and talking
about? When the office gets large enough, wouldn't it be a
better idea for him to ask a company specializing in such
work to send him an experienced operator who will work as
a clerk, and make a daily report on the attitude of the other
employees? I know an orchestra leader who doesn't hesitate
to ask a cellist or trombonist to tell him what is going on
among the other artists.

"Thousands of men and women have been discharged
because of adverse reports made on them by professional
undercover operators," the Chief continued. "If Bob, the
first assistant in the paint shop, states that the new man is a

loafer and a petty thief, and the boss fires him, is his discharge any less disconcerting because it came about at the hands of an amateur? Has anyone checked up on Bob? Isn't it possible that Bob was a little bit jealous of the new man and decided this would be an easy way to get rid of him? From what I have seen of both amateur and professional spies I would a damn sight rather have my own actions reported by the paid observer who has no axe to grind.

"It is my honest opinion that every plant in the country indulges in espionage among its employees to some extent, and, the larger the plant, the more there is of it. Some of the biggest companies have a department set up for this very purpose and a large number of men who are kept busy doing exactly the same work as that performed by our shop operators and outside men. I say this is my 'honest opinion,' and it is backed up by positive knowledge, gained through working for such firms, or having them tell me about their own departments which do the same thing."

Returning to our discussion of the local plants, we came to the name of a company that made milk products for infants. The Chief told me to pay no attention to this shop, and I asked the reason. The place had about two hundred men, and I might have been able to turn something up if I went out to see it.

"No, not out there," said the Chief definitely, "It's a long story, but I'll tell you the high spots. About twenty years ago, I got a call from the old gentleman who founded the business. When I got there, he was in a peck of trouble.

Every man in the plant had gone on strike three days before, and they were holding him up for a whacking big wage increase. If he paid it, he would eventually have to go out of business—unless he raised the price of his product, which was impossible. His goods were sold on long-term contracts, and he was committed to making deliveries at a certain price for the duration of these contracts. He had figured his labor cost at the prevailing scale when he accepted the business, and the demanded increase in wages of twenty per cent would ruin him.

"I asked the president how it had all come about and the story went like this. One morning his secretary came in to say that three men were waiting to see him. He didn't even inquire who they were, but asked to have them brought in. He was that sort of a fellow.

"One introduced himself as the general organizer for the Milk Manufacturers' Union or some such name. It was a Federal union and the only one in the country. The others were officers of the same outfit. None of them were his own employees. They announced that they had just finished organizing the plant, and had called to discuss wages and working conditions.

"The upshot of it was that they gave the president forty-eight hours to accept their demands or have a strike. He took the strike. Now he wanted me to tell him what to do. I studied the situation for two days and advised him to accept the terms exactly as submitted. Then, I agreed to put the union out of business before the contract had expired. He did, and I did. He signed up right away and within six months the union was a painful memory to everyone who had been connected with it.

"Now this was my reason for advising him as I did," said the Chief emphatically: "The work in his shop was just difficult enough to make it impractical to hire and train a new crew in a reasonable length of time. He would have lost a lot of money breaking the strike in that manner.

"We knew exactly how much he would lose by taking back the old men and paying the new rate. He had sufficient surplus to pay the increased wage scale for at least a year without being pinched for working capital. I was absolutely sure the union could be wrecked by that time, and then he could pay whatever wages he desired.

"When we finally threw the union out, the old chap told me that never again, so long as he was in business, would he operate his plant without having at least one of my men there to tip him off if another set of organizers came around. He has retired now, but his two sons carry on the business. I see the elder son once in a while, and he tells me that at least once a month the old man asks the son if our man is still there. They have fire insurance to protect themselves against fire loss, employers' liability to protect them in case of accidents among the workers. They have cyclone insurance, flywheel insurance, plate-glass insurance; and last, but not least, positive assurance from me that some morning a bunch of thugs won't walk in and say, 'Increase wages twenty per cent, or we'll call a strike.'

[118]

"And remember this, the committee of three were not even his own employees. He had never seen them before. They had just looked around the country for a soft snap, and his plant was the place they selected. They worked under cover, and the owner of the business never had the slightest inkling of what was going on until he was handed a list of demands by the committee. What's the difference between doing this and putting a pistol up to a man's head and saying, 'Your money or your life?'

"If a gangster holds you up, you can call on the law for help," the Chief added, "or, if you are strong enough and quick enough, you are at liberty to beat him up yourself. If you do that, you will be hailed as a public benefactor and a brave and courageous citizen. And I have read of business men who repelled the organizing efforts of union leaders with physical violence and they are still respected in the community. But as soon as it becomes known that a corporation hires me to keep the owners informed as to what is going on among the workmen, they are in danger of being boycotted by a large section of our society including ministers, politicians, and a lot of long-haired social workers. You can't convince such people by argument. The only way they will learn is to give them charge of a plant equipped with a lot of expensive machinery and five hundred assorted workmen. If they don't let out a yell for some real information about what is going on out in the shop before they have had the job three months, I'll get out of business and start peddling shoe strings."

[119]

Surprisingly enough, the Chief had an extremely high regard for the individual workman. "If your ordinary workman is left alone," I have heard him say, "he gets into very little trouble. But when men work in a group, you'll find one lazy man, and one crook, and one parasite who curry favor with the foreman. A trio such as that will take the starch out of the whole bunch unless they are handled by a foreman who is above the average. Foremen above the average are rare. They don't stay foremen very long. The only practical method anyone has found so far is to have an operator in the crowd who will intelligently and honestly report exactly what is going on. The good workman thrives under this protection and the malcontents have to reform or get run off the job."

CHAPTER 18

Covering Up

ONE of my principal worries at first had been the possibility of being exposed, or "turned up." Almost every
day of my first year as a labor spy had been marked by some
incident that had given me cause to consider this possibility
seriously. With the passing of time, however, these fears
disappeared; and shortly after getting established in Centerville I had put all such thoughts out of my head.

Shortly after I had become a delegate to the Central Labor
Union, I received a long letter from the Chief. I read it
hurriedly, and then went over it with the greatest care. It
had to do with an operator whom I never had met, but of
whom I had heard many times. He was regarded as an out-
standingly capable man. The letter was as follows:

"15 August, 19—.
"Dear GT-99:
   "Several times you have heard me speak of GF-14,

LABOR SPY

who is one of the first men I employed when I started
in business and he has been with me ever since. For
six years he has been on an operation like yours in
a town of about 100,000. He was vice president of the
CLU, and vice president of the Street Railway Employees Union. He was unquestionably one of the biggest labor leaders in his part of the country and was
admired and respected by both capital and labor.

"GF-14 worked for the Street Railway Company
in this town for about one year. At the end of that
time, he had reduced the power of the union to such
an extent that it was most improbable there would be
any strike for a long time to come. Our client was
about to cancel the service when I arranged with him
and some of the other employers of the city to retain
the services of GF-14 in a capacity just like yours. He
was to remain a member of his union and continue to
attend meetings. He was also to become a delegate to
the CLU and get acquainted with other union leaders
and report what was going on in the other unions of
the city. He served in this capacity for five years and
our clients were delighted with his work. He averted
at least six major strikes and was instrumental in
completely breaking up four local unions.

"When GF-14 quit his job with the street railway
company he had to find a cover so as to have an excuse
for hanging around the town any longer. He claimed
to have made a connection with a company which pub-
lishes books and he was supposed to do some house to
house canvassing and also to train and supervise a
crew of book salesmen. He reported to our office that
this was what he had done but on looking back over
his reports I do not find any record of the name of the
company he was supposed to work for. Every once in
a while he would make mention in his reports that he

[122]

was still selling books but not making a very good thing out of it.

"This brings us to the present time. After the regular CLU meeting last week, the president of the organization announced that the executive committee of the CLU would meet in a private room. GF-14 as vice president of the CLU was a member of this committee and he joined the five or six other men for the conference. You have probably read the report of what happened in the labor press. It was sent out to all the labor papers in the country and the AFL paper, *The Federationist,* also carried the story. Apparently the president of the CLU asked GF-14 what he did for a living. The operator replied that he sold books. The president then asked whom he represented or whom he worked for and GF-14 made a sorry picture as he tried to explain his business.

"It now appears to be certain that GF-14 was a first class liar. He certainly had no connection with any book house or any other business firm at the time he was put on the spot by the CLU officers and I am inclined to think he never had any such connection during all the five years he was there. Apparently the executive committee gave him 24 hours in which to produce some credentials and during all of this time he was accompanied by two guards who were union men. GF-14 was unable to produce anything at all in the way of credentials so at the end of 24 hours, a special meeting of the CLU was called and GF-14 was made to stand up in front of the crowd while the president exposed him. In his remarks, the president said there were many indications to the effect that GF-14 was an operator for a detective agency but he was unable to furnish any proof and of course this was fortunate.

"GF-14 disappeared and has not been heard from

[123]

since. We do not believe he suffered any physical violence although it is a wonder he did not. I believe he simply ran away and so far as I am concerned, this suits me right down to the ground as I never want to see him again.

"Here is what happened in my opinion. GF-14 probably got some kind of a job when he left the employ of the street railway company but his salary from us as outside man was sufficient for his needs and he let his cover slide and eventually dropped it altogether. He probably told his labor friends occasionally that he sold books but at last it became apparent to them that he had no regular vocation and naturally they became suspicious as to how he made a living.

"Here is what I want you to do within 48 hours, and this is an order. There is no doubt in my mind but what you are actively engaged in the real estate business and you have showed me plenty of proof. However, because of the publicity given to GF-14, every man in the United States who is actively connected with the labor movement but is not working at his trade is going to be under suspicion for a few months. Therefore, I want you to display positive proof of your business connection to at least three of your fellow delegates to the CLU and I want this done within 48 hours.

"This is probably the most important letter I have ever written you, GT-99, and I know you will cooperate to the utmost.

"Very truly yours,
"CHI."

As may be supposed, such a picture of disaster made a profound impression. I realized full well that the Chief was not suspecting me of doing anything along similar lines. On several occasions I had asked him for advice in connection with my real-estate business and had shown him numerous pieces of documentary evidence which proved that I was employed. At the same time, I took his instructions literally and followed them out the very day I received the letter.

There was to be a little party that same evening at the home of the president of the stove mounters' union. I phoned three of the delegates of the CLU who were also going to this party and invited them to have dinner with me, suggesting that we meet at my office.

The real-estate firm with which I was connected had a large general office where every broker had a desk. These desks were generally vacant during the day but late in the afternoon the brokers came in to get their mail and receive any instructions the boss might have for us.

When my three labor friends arrived, there were at least a dozen men in the office and I introduced the delegates to all of them. Right at that time, I was being kidded by the rest of the office about a deal I was trying to make in behalf of three elderly sisters who wished to sell their farm. The deal was practically consummated and was a most profitable one for me and the office. The other brokers razzed me unceasingly about the numerous phone calls I received from these three ladies and told my labor friends I would have to marry at least two of them in order to close the deal.

There could have been no lingering doubt in the minds of

my associates that I was a realtor. There was the added evidence that I had sold at least a dozen lots to members of labor unions. I also ran a card in the weekly newspaper sponsored by the CLU.

CHAPTER 19

Scare

IN NOVEMBER Adam Wilson, one of the most popular
laborites in the city, passed on. We all turned out for
his funeral, and it was the biggest affair of the kind I ever
saw. He had been active in every branch of union work for
fifteen years. In that time he had held various offices in his
lodge; he was a past president of the Central Labor Union,
past president of the State Federation of Labor, delegate to
numerous international conventions and to meetings of the
AFL.

This was all before my time. When I met him, he was a
paid official of his international union and away on business
most of the time. He came home every few months, and
while in the city he could walk into any of our local lodges
and be sure of a welcome. At his funeral tributes were paid
by all classes. The AFL sent a representative, the governor
of the state came in person and all ranks of society turned

out to honor his memory. After his death his wife continued to live in their old home. They had no children.

At the final CLU meeting of the year I noticed a certain tension on the part of the officers before the chair called us to order. In the early days of my work such a situation invariably caused a few chills to migrate up and down the spine, but I had adopted a fatalistic attitude on the subject. What was to be, was to be, and when it came time for me to be exposed I would face the music. Until then, let the dance go on. Accordingly, I was my usual cheerful self and joked and circulated among the crowd as usual.

The meeting started and nothing much happened under the usual order of business until it came time for a report from the grievance committee. The chairman was an elderly chap named Greeley. He ran a small cigar factory which employed about ten men, and he and his employees and a few others from outside shops constituted the cigar makers' local. He read his report carefully and as it went on, you could hear the hearts of most of the crowd pounding, or at least it seemed that way.

"Brother president and brothers," he began, "I herewith submit the monthly report of your grievance committee and move its adoption." The president asked him to come up on the platform. It seems as if I can still hear him reading in his harsh, clear voice.

"Your grievance committee has, during the past month, received certain information of a most astonishing nature. We investigated it thoroughly and found the reports to be as represented in every way. In addition thereto, we have been fortunate in discovering other sources of information and have uncovered facts which are more damning than any we had dreamed of. It is my sad duty to reveal them to you at this time.

"Men fortunate enough to belong to labor unions have ever prided themselves on living in accordance with the Golden Rule whether they were active members of any religious body or not. The American Federation of Labor and all its constituent branches has an enviable record in this regard which is engraved on the pages of American history. It has been our joyous privilege in this city to emulate the example of our leaders and live in honorable and peaceable harmony with our neighbors. What a terrible thing it is then, to find that for long we have harbored in our midst one who not only failed to live up to his obligation as a union man in his personal life but used his high position to betray his fellows."

The day the Chief hired me was the first time. The night the Argonne fight started was the second time. I promised a third time and here it is. The same crawly sensation way down inside. The same taste in my mouth.

"During our association with the erring brother," Greeley continued, "he conveyed information to numerous anti-union employers to the effect that designated men and women on their payrolls were either members of, or applying for admission to, various local unions of this city. This information invariably led to the dismissal of said employees. He also caused information as to the acts of the officers of his lodge

[129]

to be given to the employers of the community and thereby caused the union movement to suffer. As a member of this Central Labor Union he repeatedly passed on to the opposition reports of our business transactions and discussions and thus betrayed the confidence placed in him and which he was sworn to maintain inviolate. The evidence in support of these various allegations has been placed before the executive committee of this organization and the local and international union to which the culprit belonged and has been acknowledged as bona fide and correct. It is therefore requested that the membership excuse us from reading said evidence in open meeting lest there be present another Judas who will sell our secrets for dirty silver."

I could still make a dash for the door. There was one in front that led to the fire escape. The main entrance was in the rear. I could not make the back one but the fire escape was a possibility. I would try it. No, I couldn't move. My legs wouldn't work. Nothing to do but face it. Greeley had paused for a moment while he took a drink from the glass that always stood on the desk. Now he continued in the same even tone.

"In conclusion, it is hereby resolved that the name of the wayward brother be stricken from the minute books of this body wherever it does appear, and from this time forth his name shall never again be spoken by us or our successors except at the final December meeting of this Central Labor Union each year when this report in its entirety shall be read by the then chairman of your grievance committee as a solemn warning to all who hear. The name of the betrayer is Adam Wilson. Respectfully submitted by your grievance committee. Paul T. Greeley, Chairman."

My God! Adam Wilson! The biggest labor leader in the state and hardly cold in his grave.

CHAPTER 20

Aftermath

N° ONE said a word for what seemed a long time after Greeley finished. When I finally looked around, the first person my eyes rested on was the delegate of the garment workers. He looked like a cadaver. Drift-pin Ike, the iron workers' delegate, sat next to Morry. He had been complaining about insufficient heat in the hall before the meeting started but in spite of this, Andy's high stiff collar lay in soggy folds around the base of his long neck. None of the other fellows looked much better. This doesn't mean that they were spies. In similar circumstances, at a meeting of a bar association, or a ministers' alliance, mothers' club or college fraternity, almost every member would have the thought, "I wonder if they've found out about that." The "that" might be relatively unimportant, but a conscience can be a terrible thing at times.

Every man there was sworn to secrecy until the following

day, when the executive committee would turn the matter over to the newspapers and the CLU weekly sheet.

As soon as the meeting adjourned I drove to a town thirty miles away and phoned the Chief. I took it for granted that Wilson had been one of our operators, and that after he had progressed into the international field I had been sent to replace him.

"No, he's not our man and never was," the Chief said. "For a long time we have been pretty sure he was an operator but we never did anything about it. I suspect he worked for the same group of clients we do. They often have a couple of agencies to be sure everything is covered. The history of those cases is that the papers get the story and it makes quite a stink. I'll get hold of our clients tonight and tell them about it. They have a good deal of drag and can probably hush it up after a day or two."

He could tell from my manner that I was pretty badly shaken, and advised me to take a few days off and get hold of myself. "You're a full-fledged operator now that this has happened," the Chief remarked. "You've had every experience an op can have except one. You haven't fluked yet." That remark made me pretty sore, but later I figured out why he had said it. If I had been thinking of walking off the job, this crack might have made me mad enough to change my mind.

When I hung up, I sat in the booth for a good many minutes thinking. Then I walked around for a while, and went into a phone booth in an old, ratty hotel.

"Let me talk to Mrs. Adam Wilson in Centerville," I told the operator.

"This is a friend of your husband," I said when a sweet, subdued voice answered. "I was one of the *real* friends of your husband, Mrs. Wilson, and I know *all* about *all* of his activities." I spoke slowly and distinctly and with all the sincerity I could muster. I didn't have to try hard for I was in dead earnest.

"There was a meeting of the CLU tonight, Mrs. Wilson, and the chairman of the grievance committee, Mr. Greeley, whom you probably know, read quite a long report about your husband and his secret work. The CLU is turning the matter over to the newspapers tomorrow. You don't know me but I am in the same business your husband was. I'm calling to tell you about this so you can get away if you want to. If there's someone you could go to visit until you see how this comes out I'll help you get there."

There was silence from the other end of the wire and I thought she had hung up, or fainted, so I said, "Hello."

"I'm listening," she said, "and trying to think. I don't know whether you are what you claim to be or not, but I've expected a message like this for over twenty years. When he died I thought there was no need to worry about it any longer. I decided what to do long ago and I can still do it. Thanks for calling and—wait a minute. I don't know who you are, but I don't think anyone would fool me about a thing like this. When your turn comes, and they all get

[134]

turned up in the end, I hope someone will give your missus the tip-off in time. Good-by and good luck."

Starting back to my car, I only got part way when I had to sit down on the curb, just about as sick as I'd ever been in my life.

The newspapers made quite a story out of it, but people soon forgot—all except me and such other spies as there were in the community. Two of our Centerville shop operators quit without a word to anyone.

CHAPTER 21

Strike

IN JANUARY I had been on this assignment a year and was therefore eligible to accept an office in the electrical workers' local. I was rewarded by my union friends with the position of vice president, which automatically made me a member of the executive committee, and thus aware of all plans being made for the lodge. This was indeed a stroke of good fortune as it brought me in touch with the hottest piece of news I had uncovered so far.

"I'm glad your year of probation is up," said Burdette, our president, on the night of my first meeting with the executive committee. "We have just undertaken a big job and you can give us a lot of help. As you know, most of our members are in the construction end of the business, but this only includes one half of the electricians in the city. The other half are with the Electric Light and Power Company which has always been open shop. Brother Hinds, one of our international organizers, has been working under cover for two months and he has actual applications and initiation fees from fifty-seven of these power company men. As of tonight, he has signed up thirty-one linesmen, fourteen groundmen, three cable splicers, and nine men from the installation department. There are about four hundred eligible men in all, and as soon as he has about one hundred of them he is going to have a big initiation and come out into the open to get the other three hundred. You are a good talker and we are counting on you to do your share of the public speaking. Hinds is an expert on looking up men in their homes, and talking to them on the job, but neither he nor any of the rest of our officers is much account when it comes to handing out a hot line before a crowd."

Here was a fine kettle of fish. The Light and Power Company was not a client. The Manufacturers' Association had never been able to make them come into the group which supported me. No sir, they knew their business. Their men were loyal. If an organizer came within sight of one of their line crews it wouldn't be ten minutes until the foreman called the president of the company and told him about it. It should be added that Hinds wasn't even coming around union headquarters, and the only local man he communicated with was Burdette, the president. He was a smooth worker with a big job, and he was doing it in the right way—until I put the skids under him.

The Chief went to see the power company, but had no luck

in getting any business. They didn't believe his story and simply weren't interested. He asked if they would talk to him if he gave them names and they said they would.

He told me to get him the names of at least four men who had filed applications, but the only person who had a list was Hinds and I hadn't yet been able to meet him.

The Chief had given me twenty-four hours to produce. Driving around until I found a line crew in the employ of the power company, I pretended to have engine trouble. They helped me out. I had a camera in the car, and offered to take their picture as a group and mail them prints. They fell for this, and I got their names and addresses. I did this with three other crews the same morning.

That afternoon I hot-footed it around to these very same addresses and tried to sell vacant lots to the wives or mothers. In the course of my talk we discussed unions without any mention of my being a union man and of course I said nothing about knowing their men folks, or how I happened to call. Several women got real chatty, and the net result was the names of three union linemen and one groundman out of the nine places I visited. I might have gotten more, but only four were required, and I quit as soon as they were obtained.

The Chief had these in time for his appointment. Now the power people showed interest and promised they would give him some work if they found he was correct and the four men actually had applied for membership. The personnel manager made his investigation by calling the four on the carpet individually and asking them about it. Two said, "Yes," and two said, "No."

The Chief moaned and tore his hair when he heard of the dumb way they had handled the affair. By that time I had seven more names, and three of these "confessed." The men who admitted union connections were fired forthwith because they would not promise to give up the union. As a result we got a fine large contract to protect the lords of light and power from the blight of union domination.

If the personnel man had been a little more subtle, we would have had a much easier job. The thing to have done was to lay off or discharge union men a few at a time, or as fast as they were recruited. One can always find a good excuse to fire a man on account of some mistake or carelessness in his work. Now, however, it was noised about on all sides that the bosses were aware of Hinds's work and both sides came out into the open.

Hinds worked fast. That very day he had quarter-page ads in the papers announcing that five light and power employees had been summarily dismissed for no greater crime than applying for membership in a union. He appealed for popular support. The light and power people countered by presenting "yellow dog" agreements to all employees and asking them to sign or quit. The "yellow dog" contract provided that the employee who signed it would not join a labor organization so long as he or she remained on the payroll. It was couched in more elegant terms, but this is the gist of the thing, and has been so held in court. Most of the men with union connections refused to sign, and this was a compliment to the work of Hinds. He had been keeping in personal touch with all the men he had signed up, and had taught them the basic principles of unionism in the right way. He had them lined up so well that they were willing to stand for a strike rather than change their minds. As is usual in such cases, the stand-patters with the union were mostly the younger men or those without families.

The same day that the ads appeared we had an extraordinary session of the lodge and initiated about fifty light and power employees who had been fired for refusing to sign the "yellow dog." The lodge then went into executive session and called a strike. There was no other alternative in such a case, and neither I nor a hundred other operators could have stopped a strike at this time. We didn't even have time to get any of our people in the company payroll, so they could go on strike with the rest of the crew and thus attend meetings, do picket duty, keep in touch with the rank and file, and see what the individual striker thought about the matter.

CHAPTER 22

Pitchmen to the Rescue

A PUBLIC utility strike is about the worst kind there is. Regardless of who is right the public suffers a lot of inconvenience and is pretty short-tempered about it. Also, electricity being what it is, a lot of damage can be done in short order. The first day of the strike a crew of hoodlums went around the city throwing lengths of chain over many of the high tension wires. This shorted them and they burned through. Loose ends fell to the ground, and a public menace was created. In addition, a section of the city was without current until the lines were repaired. The regular linemen, who could have repaired these breaks in a few minutes were all on strike. The company accused the strikers, and the strikers accused the company of doing it to influence public opinion. Both sides were innocent. It really was a gang of toughs.

To make matters worse, I never saw a worse late winter

and early spring. Snow and rain, and then it would freeze everything up solid. Lines down all over the place, and makeshift crews unable to repair them.

The company was lucky in that very few central-station men walked out. This meant that the men who made the electricity by firing the boilers, running the turbines and dynamos, and operating the enormous control boards that start the flow of current on its way to homes and factories were still at their posts. To insure their staying there, dormitories were at once opened in the stations, and the employees remained there twenty-four hours a day. It was the field men, linemen, groundmen, pole setters, and all the rest who were responsible for leading the wattage from the dynamos to the motors, vacuum cleaners, and living-room lights, who were striking.

The company was a unit of one of the enormous public utility chains that operated under a score of different names in various states and cities. The logical place to get replacements was from other units of the group, and this was done. On the second day they arrived, and the job of clearing up the mess was started. The Chief sent in a few strike-breakers also. Union men picketed all strike-breaking crews, and once each hour one of the pickets would read aloud the motion passed by the local, authorizing the strike. The strike-breakers listened, and there were a few defections. It had been strictly ordered that no violence should occur.

In the meantime a publicity man had arrived from international electrical union headquarters and none of the union officers spoke for publication until it had been approved by the press agent. Paid ads went into the press every day to advise the public on the union side of the situation. The company countered in the same manner. Ten days passed with both sides sitting tight. A few of the imported men from the other power companies joined the strikers, and a few of the strikers went back to work.

The men had three days' pay coming when the strike started, and they collected this at the company offices on the regular pay-day without any trouble. Then the first regular pay-day came around. My mind went back, as it always did at such times, to those New England strikes before the war and the twelve payless pay-days they had seen. Workingmen and their families are the same the world over in one respect. When Dad comes home on pay-night, the children are always on good behavior. Mother smiles a little brighter and the old man feels he's not such a bad old scout after all. But when Dad comes home on a striking pay-night, things are different. Every member of the family tries to keep from thinking about what might happen if there never were another pay envelope. John and Mary fail to get their regular spending money, and mother wonders what she is going to say to the grocer if he asks her to pay the weekly bill. Each succeeding payless pay-day is worse.

As was expected, a little spontaneous violence took place that night. Some of the men tried to drown their sorrows, and ended up the evening by burning down a few lines and destroying a little company property.

The following day the Chief countered by starting what he called his "defeatist brigade."

A pitchman is a street vendor who displays his wares on a small table near the curb, and all the while keeps up an endless flow of chatter to attract attention to himself and his wares. Don't waste any pity on these chaps. They are pretty shrewd and have a lot more brains and dollars than the general public suspects or would believe. They drift north in summer and south in winter and lead a splendid imitation of the "life of Riley."

The Chief corralled twelve of those fellows and turned them loose on the homes of the strikers. The list of addresses was furnished by the company. The stunt was pulled this way.

"Good morning, madam," a pitchman would say when a wife answered his ring. "I have the honor to present you three cakes of Crowell's soap which is just being put on the market. Please understand that I am not selling this article, and even if you desired to buy some, it is not yet for sale. The manufacturer has adopted a wise and farsighted policy in the matter of placing this new soap within reach of the consumer. I am only one of several hundred men and women who are calling on housewives on a similar mission. We are giving you the soap and only request that you use it in your home in the usual way. Use it for bathing. Use it in the laundry. Use it in the kitchen. In a week I will call again. No, not to ask you to buy some—I am grieved at being misjudged, madam. Not to sell any, but to ask you if you ever used a better soap for all purposes in your life. We want the opinion of the American housewife before putting this soap on the market, so that it will be a proven fact that we are giving her just what she wants."

He would ramble on in this vein for awhile and then pull out his book to make a note of the name and address—and the occupation of the man of the house. "Oh, an employee of the Light & Power Company. Not on strike I hope. Ah, dear me. That is indeed unfortunate. Madam, you see before you an example of what comes from letting one of these union organizers talk men into joining a union. Five years ago I was happily employed in Squeedunk, the head of a charming family with a little house like yours almost paid for. Our children were graduating from high school and we fondly hoped to send them to the state university. Then what happened? I had the wool pulled over my eyes by a man who claimed to be my friend and the friend of every honest working man in the employ of my company. He induced us to join a labor union and within a year where was I? Out of my job! Out of my home! My wife seeking shelter with her family and my children at work in the mines instead of gaining an education in the university. That is what a labor union did to me." And so forth.

The reason for the Chief's hiring pitchmen was that nowhere else in the world could he find men who looked so much like workingmen, in addition to being able to put on an act so convincingly.

After a couple of days of this, the Chief had them working the railroad stations, office buildings and other public places.

[145]

Two pitchmen would enter an elevator and greet each other as friends. To the casual observer, they would be business men and possibly tenants of the building. The conversation would go like this.

"Hello, Bert."

"Hello, Alf."

"Got any electricity out at your house these days, Bert?"

"All the time, Alf. How's it out your way?"

"Just the same as usual, Bert. No trouble at all. I guess the strikers are pretty sick of the deal. I was down to the station this morning and saw one of them, a chap I went to grammar school with. He's leaving town with five or six others to look for another job, and you should hear him cuss out the union."

"Strikes never were good for much, Alf."

"You're right. Well, I'm getting out here. S'long, Bert."

"S'long, Alf."

This went on all over town for a week. It made a tremendous impression on the public and at the end of that time, another payless day arrived.

CHAPTER 23

Finks for the Finish

M Y PART in all this was comparatively slight. Each day there was a rally for the strikers at noon when they were addressed by Hinds, and as many other big laborites as he could line up. Frequently I was called on to fill in. These sessions are a part of every strike and are supposed to help the men keep their courage up and send them back to the picket line with a stern resolve to win.

Outside of speaking at these meetings I roved around and picked up as much information as I could and passed it on to the Chief, who deemed this strike of such importance that he had come down himself and established headquarters in one of the hotels under an assumed name. He had several unlisted phones in his suite and I habitually called him every three hours whether I had anything to report or not.

All the while I was looking for the chance to spring my big act. The regular monthly business meeting of the local was held the night following the second payless day. Some of our pitchmen friends had been instructed to suggest to the wives of the strikers that they should go to union headquarters and demand money; the union had taken their husbands' jobs and should pay them.

The business agent was around the office all day, as he kept regular office hours, and he had been driven crazy by women clamoring for money. He reported this at the meeting and moved that a sum of money be set aside to help the most needy cases. No union ever likes to start a strike unless it has enough money in the treasury to pay unemployed benefits to its members for what it considered the maximum duration of a strike. This is a rather vague statement, and different unions interpret it in different ways. The grand lodge had sent us a little money but this had been used at once for newspaper advertising.

The situation was far from pleasant from the point of view of our original members. The older members were all working in the building trade, and they had little in common with this crew of linemen. While Hinds had been doing his undercover organizing it had been assumed that the linemen would eventually be segregated into a lodge of their own, but we would give them a roof while they were getting their legs under them. And here they were, a lot of poor relations with a peck of troubles, clamoring for us to pull their chestnuts out of the fire.

I decided the stage was set.

"Brothers," I said when the chair recognized me, "we

electricians are fortunate in our calling. A knowledge of our trade enables us to regulate and control the most gigantic storehouse of power in the universe. Our greatest scientists state candidly that they do not know exactly how to define force of any kind. When they get to talking about electromotive force they simply throw up their hands and quit. We, the practical scientists, however, have solved the problem of how to handle this force and we are doing it all over the world with precision, with safety, and in such a manner as to bless mankind.

"As we sit here this evening, I am wondering if we are handling our personal problems with the same care and forethought we exercise in our trade. I am tempted to say that if we handled a 2200-volt line with the same lack of thought we have shown in another matter the death benefit fund would soon show a deficit.

"Brothers, I refer to the handling of this entire strike problem so far as this local is concerned. This powerful affair came upon us without warning. There was no circuit breaker. We have got hold of it and like the man holding the lion's tail we can't hang on, and we can't let go. It's too late for forethought, but I look upon it as a courageous thing to stop right now and see what we've gotten ourselves into."

I then rehashed the whole thing. Sympathy was shown for the strikers; Hinds had done a fine job, but had run into bad luck in having to display his hand when only half ready. I figured how long the funds in our treasury would last if we started paying strike benefits, and stressed the fact that the motion on the floor right now was on this very subject, and to consider my words well before voting in support of it.

I then balled the whole thing up by offering an amendment to the motion, to the effect that the granting of the funds suggested by the business agent should be contingent on the linemen's resigning from our lodge and forming a local of their own. To show my sincerity, I pledged my entire time for a month to assist them in getting under way if they decided to resign.

This offer squared me with Hinds, who had decided I was simply trying to break the strike.

My talk and the amendment brought on a hot discussion which lasted about two hours in spite of the efforts of the president to stop it. The amount of money suggested by the business agent was only five hundred dollars and we all knew how far a new lodge with all the members on strike could get on this. It had been pretty well established that the international union would give them nothing more.

And there was another, and far more significant side to the affair. The business agent was an important figure, and when he made his motion it had been taken for granted on all sides that it would carry. When I bucked him, it became a personal issue between us. If his motion failed to carry, he was in the same spot as that in which a French minister finds himself when one of his bills in the senate is defeated. He must resign, for the body no longer has confidence in him. The business agent didn't want to resign,

[150]

and as man after man spoke along the lines I had advocated he got more and more uncomfortable.

"Brothers," he finally said in desperation, "I want to assure you I had no idea of starting such a debate when I made my original motion. It seemed a practical thing to do, and I will admit it had not been the subject of careful thought and study. Here is what I now propose: With the consent of the seconder of my original motion, I will withdraw it if the brother who offered the amendment and his seconder will do the same."

This was done. The battle ended in a parliamentary draw, but with an actual victory for me, and a defeat for the small faction who were sponsoring the strike. The union, so far as the old members were concerned, lost all interest in the strike after that night; and this was a big feature in speeding the final windup.

The union lost this strike as unions lost hundreds, maybe thousands of others, through inability to make full and complete preparations in advance. Credit is due in part to the labor spy.

The men started to ask for their old jobs back during the third week. The company took back the ones it wished—if they signed the "yellow dog" contract, and the others were told to move on.

The strike-breakers furnished by us were laid off, and the others were shipped back to the companies from whence they came. The best recruiting grounds for strike-breakers were in Chicago and New York where they managed to exist in flop houses and on park benches between strikes.

The Chief and our other people have told me endless tales about this seemingly necessary adjunct to American industry—the "fink." Superficially he is just a big hulk with a little brutal courage. To be an all-around fink a man must be able to start and stop a street-car, operate an elevator, swing a pick, and push a truck. That is the extent of his required vocational experience. While engaged in strike-breaking he gets eight dollars a day and up, with board and weapons. An experienced fink can average ten dollars' worth of plunder every day of his employment, "even in a stone quarry," as the saying goes. To make a guess as to his additional income when engaged on a striking street-car line, or in a factory, would be impossible. And yet, despite all this munificence they are back on their park benches within a week of the ending of a strike.

One time I asked the Chief why he objected to letting the strike-breakers he furnished work as guards. "When you hand a man a weapon and tell him to guard something," he said, "you have got to assume that the time will come when he will use that weapon. If your man is highly intelligent he will use discretion. But highly intelligent men are not working as strike-breakers. Highly intelligent men are working in shops, and offices, and on railroad trains or ships, and not loafing around waiting for a strike to start so they can get a few days work as a guard or strike-breaker. No matter what you tell a guard his first thought is to protect himself, and not to protect the property of our client. If he thinks he is in danger he is more apt to get panicky and start shooting than not. Anyone may get killed, and I don't want it on my conscience. My job is to prevent strikes, not to break them after some ignoramus lets them get under way.

"Strike-breaking is the most expensive luxury in the world. And it's absolutely unnecessary. The linemen's strike cost the power company enough to have secured protection, such as I can furnish them, for at least twenty years. Before this thing began the president wouldn't even let me into his office. When the strike actually started I became the greatest man in the world. Nothing was too good for me. Expense be damned. Stop the strike. Break the union. Do something. Do anything, but do it quick.

"As a matter of fact it's bad enough when you furnish only strike-breakers," he continued. "All finks are about the same, which means they are terrible. They're worse than any-one outside the business has any idea of. No decent workman will take a job as a fink; so you get the other kind. He'll cheat and steal and lie from the minute he comes to the job until he leaves. I always tell our clients this is the kind of man I am getting for them, and that is all I or anyone else can get. They say, 'That's perfectly all right. We understand. Do the best you can.' But when the job is over and the client gets back to normal, he gets to thinking about the gang of thugs I rang in on him. He yells to high heaven, and says he has been stung. I've even had them try to get out of paying all the bill. That's why I collect daily when I furnish finks. Getting mixed up in a strike is one of the best ways I know of to lose your standing in the community.

"There are a couple of manufacturers in the country who can't quit talking about me and the trimming I gave them when they had a strike. Both of these fellows saw me every day of their strike and they approved everything I did. They kept telling me to do the best I could and I needn't come to them at all, just get the damn' thing settled. But as soon as they got back to normal and they saw what a mess the strike-breakers had made of their nice factories, they blamed it all on me. I even had a list of damages made out every day all through the strike, and gave this to the clients with a letter explaining how and why everything had happened, but I might just as well have torn the paper up and scattered it to the winds. If you ever get to selling our service, don't take any strike jobs if you can help it."

In forty days, the light and power business was back to normal. The Chief told me the expense to the client from all sources, such as damages, lawsuits, loss of current sales and our charges, was three hundred thousand dollars. This was paid out of earnings and the stockholders footed the bill in the end. Some four hundred men lost four weeks' pay, which amounted to sixty-five thousand dollars. Had the union won, the men would have still lost the pay. The strike was only for the reinstatement of a few men, and recognition of the union. As no wage controversy was involved, there was no hope of immediate gain in this direction.

If I had not got wind of Hinds's work, and the men had

been organized one hundred per cent before trouble started, the company would have won anyway. Electric and gas outfits were pretty hard nuts to crack in those days.

It hurts a man's self-respect to come slinking back to his job after he has struck. One wonders if he is as good a workman. His wife and kids have a different slant on Dad's employer too and they lose confidence in the future.

I probably gained more out of that mess than anyone else. I had tipped the thing off in the first place. In a pitched battle with the business agent, the strongest man in my local, I had made him back down. And there was the added general experience gained by having taken an active part in a major strike.

CHAPTER 24

Chance for Advancement

WHEN a young, ambitious man seeks employment he is very apt to inquire, "What are the chances for advancement?" I was ambitious, but at the same time I did not request this information when the Chief hired me. The feeling of confidence he inspired gave ample assurance that I would be taken care of. As time went on, however, the thought often came to me. It was uppermost in my mind when the curtains were finally drawn on the linemen's strike.

I determined to have a talk with the Chief before he left town. Every labor leader in town was my friend and confidant. I was "in on the know" at every one of the locals where trouble (strikes or an organizing drive) might crop up. For the life of me I couldn't see anything in the future except the same old rut, and I was tired of it. The real-estate job I had taken as a cover had turned out well, and I was considering quitting the Chief and starting a realty business of my own. My chance to speak up came one day when the Chief asked me to come to his hotel. I went with a fixed determination to have a definite understanding on the future.

"Sit down and get ready to listen," said the Chief when I entered his suite. He was in a hurry and later I learned the reason. He was leaving in about an hour, and it took him all of that time to dispose of me.

"When this mess started," he continued, "you had just succeeded in getting solidly intrenched in your electricians' local. Now you are a vice president and that's fine. Before I had a chance to tell you what to do about it, we were in this strike and that lost us a good deal of time. You will have to work like the dickens to make up for it. Since joining me, you have done just about everything a man is ever called on to do but you have been down with the underlings. Now I want you to get up into the higher brackets. Join the stuffed shirts. Step out with the elite. Associate with the plutocrats and the bloated aristocracy. Within one more year, I want you to have a dozen presidents of international unions calling you by your first name. If you can call them by their first names, too, so much the better; but they are to be calling you by yours no matter what happens.

"You're in a better position than any of our boys have ever been when starting out on a job of this sort," he went on impressively. "Adam Wilson, the old chap who died and was then turned up, was the strongest labor leader in the state. He controlled the labor vote for at least four years. No one has been able to replace him and, luckily, there are no very likely candidates for his position. The bunch clamoring for it now are all crooks and the history of organized labor is that no crook ever lasted very long when he got to the top of the heap. Labor politics is different from other politics in this respect.

"Now the very first thing you've got to do is grab complete control of this bunch of electricians you belong to. Every big laborite got his start by being the absolute boss of his local, and don't you forget it. You run the clerks' local but that's so small it doesn't amount to much. This guy Bradley, your business agent, is undisputed boss of the electricians. You made a bum out of him when it came to settling the strike and I want you to keep right on his tail until he's down and out. And I don't just mean until he's out of office. Chase him right out of town and let all the union men in the state know you did it. When you get rid of him, don't take his job yourself. Put *your* man into the business agent's office and then watch him closely. You won't have time to be business agent of a big local. You have over four hundred in your lodge and in any man's country, a guy with four hundred men in his pocket is entitled to respect. You get this crowd lined up and you'll be dumbfounded what a big man the other labor people think you are.

"I'm absolutely sure you can do this," the Chief went on. "I'm so sure, I want you to start doing something else at the same time. Start getting acquainted at the state capital. The president of the State Federation of Labor lives down there. This year the state labor convention will be there in August. I think you can get to be a delegate all right, but find some excuse to drop in and say hello to him several times in the next couple of months and size him up. In another year or so you are going to have his job, and it's only sensible for you to get a slant on what it amounts to.

"That's the lineup for the present and now we'll talk a little about salary. As soon as you are in complete control of your local and I can tell the light and power people you have it in the bag, I can raise you one hundred dollars a month. In addition to that, I have made a deal with a group of the biggest contractors in town, and as soon as you are in position to tell the Building Trades Council which end is up, and make them like it, there is another one-hundred-dollar raise in it for you. When you get your electricians' local under your thumb, you will be in a good position to swing all the building trades at the same time. The electricians are just about the strongest local in the Council. As the electricians' delegate to the council, Bradley is one of the two big men in the Building Trades. When you get rid of him, step right into his shoes without giving anyone else a chance to beat you to it—and there will be a big gang waiting to try."

(A Building Trades Council operates in every community. It consists of delegates from all the building trade locals and is almost as powerful as the Central Labor Union. It really is the Central Labor Union less the shop and miscellaneous trades. In our town there were thirty-eight local unions. Of these, twenty-one were in the Building Trades Council.)

We talked about details for a while and the Chief left. "I hope," he said, with the smile I had not seen all through the strike, "that I didn't interrupt any plans you might have been making for a quiet and peaccable summer. And remember this: When you get to be boss of the city and boss of the state, there are still a hell of a lot of offices in the AFL for you to consider. And while you're thinking about it, you might make some kind of a guess as to what some big employers' group like the National Association of Manufacturers would say if I went in to them and said, 'Gentlemen, I am in position to dictate the policy and acts of the entire American Federation of Labor along any lines you desire.' When you went to work for me, you would have said I was crazy if I talked that way. Now you know I'm not."

And I had come prepared to inquire about the chances a young man had to advance himself!

This conference was in marked contrast with those I had with the Chief when I was breaking in. Then, he had not only told me what to do, but how to do it. Today, he contented himself with an outline of the things to be accomplished, and left the details to me. I asked for suggestions along broad lines and he gave them. In the old days my job had been to handle men in masses and he knew with uncanny certainty how groups would react. Now, when my work was primarily with individuals, he could not give the same specific advice without an intimate knowledge of the persons with whom I was to deal. For the present, my principal concern was the business agent of my local. Since the Chief did not know him he could only give the most general advice on how I should proceed.

CHAPTER 25

Unwelcome Visitor

O NE of the functions of a labor union is to supervise apprentices and develop them into skilled mechanics before they become union members. There are usually rules governing this, and their enforcement is in the hands of a committee. In the years immediately following the war there was a great shortage of skilled labor, particularly of men who knew the shop and building trades.

This condition always means that a lot of men are drawing high wages for poor work. I suppose all local unions were lax in maintaining their trade standards at this time. I know from experience that some examining boards have been bribed to pass apprentices who had no more business working at their particular trades than I had training animals. In our lodge Bradley, the business agent, was also chairman of the committee which examined apprentices for promotion to full-fledged electricians.

The universal cry from our local contractors and subcontractors was in protest against the poor work done by the building tradesmen in general. This was aired in the newspapers occasionally and it actually was a public disgrace. I don't know whether the electricians were poorer workmen than the others, but they were in a bad way, as I soon found out for myself.

I made an exhaustive study of the local construction laws. In every large town there is a group of city ordinances, known as the building code, and I devoted myself to it. I then spent a couple of evenings with brother electricians whom I knew to be skilled workmen. Admitting my unfamiliarity with recent developments in the trade, I asked them a thousand questions on the subject, and got a world of information. Although these old-timers knew the business thoroughly, they admitted cutting a lot of corners on every job they did. Such practices would not have been tolerated if the city building inspectors and architects' representatives were really well qualified and capable. Poor inspection permitted poor work, and the public paid the bill.

Next, I called on the eight young men who had just passed our semi-annual examination and were now listed as full-fledged electricians. Five of them turned out to be pretty poor examples of what a skilled craftsman should be.

Now I was ready to start my campaign to unseat Bradley, the electricians' business agent, and kingpin of lodge 1536.

Bradley and I had never been friendly. Since the skirmish at the strike meeting he had not been speaking to me,

[163]

but I acted as if nothing had happened. His job as business agent of the local paid him three hundred dollars a month, with an expense allowance. This was a little more than he could have made working at the trade, and as business agent he had an office and was his own boss to a large extent.

Unemployed members gathered at his office early each morning. Phone calls would come in from electrical contractors for men, and Bradley would assign the waiting members in accordance to the time they had been unemployed. Calls for men seldom came in after eight o'clock, and Bradley had the rest of the day to himself.

He habitually made a number of calls on electrical contractors for the purpose of learning what jobs were coming up in the future so that he could arrange to have men ready when needed. He also visited electrical jobs in progress to estimate how long they would last and decide what to do with the workmen when the job ended.

All this was essential. A good business agent was a great help to the contractors and to the union members as well. Bradley also spent a good deal of his time hobnobbing with other business agents about the general labor situation among the building trades. This was in line of duty and not to be criticized. In short, he conducted himself just about as any business agent would in handling his job.

I suppose Bradley was as honest as most business agents. If some of the contractors insisted on giving him a gift of, say, five hundred dollars at Christmas time, who was there to prove that he assigned the best men to the donors' jobs during the ensuing year? I took it for granted that this happened and hoped sooner or later to prove it.

It was also quite probable that he got an occasional donation for permitting electricians to work on jobs where the union agreement was violated. Workmen seldom complained of such things; so nobody was the wiser. Bradley, through his office of business agent, was a sort of general manager for the members. They drew their pay and got their detailed instructions from the electrical contractor who employed them, but Bradley was the boy who told them where to work and when to work. The president of a lodge got all the glory, but he was pretty much of a figurehead. Bradley wore the brass hat.

As I analyzed the situation in an effort to find a hole in Brother Bradley's armor, all I could see on the surface was that we had a lot of pretty poor workmen. For this he was almost directly responsible. I decided to fire a few ranging shots at the next meeting of the executive committee. This was the committee which actually ran the lodge.

"It has been a number of years since I worked at the trade," I said in conversational manner when the routine business had been disposed of, and we were talking about the "good of the order," which subject never seems to be exhausted. "To keep myself informed, I have been trying to get up to date on current practice. The other night, after we initiated the eight apprentices, I asked them a few questions. I thought they would know the answers right off on account of having studied them recently. I was surprised to find they are not so well instructed as they should be. They know little about anything except the most common practices, and have but the vaguest notions regarding the city building code so far as it applies to electrical work."

"What didn't those guys know?" asked Bradley.

"I talked to them about connecting motor-generator sets," I replied, "and they seemed to think there were no special requirements for the higher voltages. Three of the boys said they would be warned by the foremen if there were any unusual precautions to take. The others didn't seem to know anything about the subject at all. I asked all of them what they knew about the changes made in the code last year regarding insulation to be used when bringing lines of various voltages through walls of different fire-resisting quality. They all replied, 'We use whatever the boss tells us to.' None of them really seemed to know anything about the matter or to be interested in whether the boss might be right or not. I'm not saying that we want a lot of men who will spend their time arguing with the foreman, but I think these fellows should know how a simple electrical job should be done."

Bradley snapped right back by saying he was responsible for the training of these kids and intimated rather pointedly it was no business of anyone else.

"I differ with Mr. Bradley," I said in the same conversational tone. "When the vice president of an electricians' lodge asks eight fellow members who are working at the trade how to bring two hundred and twenty volts through a four-inch wood and plasterboard wall and none of them can quote the code on the subject, I think it is the business of the entire lodge."

An old chap named Turner had been business agent of the lodge long ago. Eventually he resigned and became an electrical contractor. After he had made a small fortune he retired and took up his card (joined the union) again. When the bank threatened to foreclose the mortgage on Union Hall, old man Turner saved the day and the hall by lending the Central Labor Union enough money to pay off the bank. The mortgage was now in Turner's possession.

He spent most of his time loafing around the hall and every union man in town knew and liked the old gent. I met him when I first came to Centerville and he gave me a lot of the past history of the labor movement in the city which was of great use to me as time went on. He attended every meeting of the electricians' lodge and whenever he felt like it, he dropped in on the executive committee. During his active days in the lodge, he had held every office as well as having been business agent and was such a privileged character, no one on the committee would have thought of telling him to get out. He was with us this night.

"That's the best I ever heard," the old fellow said when he heard my remark. "I'm always telling you fellows you can't get real mechanics any more. That's why I quit business. I couldn't do all the work myself and I couldn't hire workmen to do it. All I got was a bunch of wirepullers and clockwatchers. Sonny, if none of these boys will tell you how it's done, come to me and I'll tell you. And I'll bet you fifty dollars I can tell you just exactly what the code specifies. I helped write that code and I know it inside out and upside down. But how about having Brad here give a little lecture on modern practice? Come on, Mr. Business Agent, tell the committee just how you would bring two hundred and twenty volts through the wall."

By Gosh! I was ready to bet Bradley didn't know himself. He looked all set to burst for a minute, and then ripped out something about it being no wonder we lost strikes with the members and even the executive committee doing nothing except sitting around trying to kid the only men in the lodge who did any work for the organization. Old man Turner got up cackling and walked around the room slapping his knees.

Finally he came up to Bradley and said, suddenly very seriously, "Bradley, I'll bet you fifty dollars that you can't answer that question, and here's my fifty. I'll let the executive committee be judge."

He slammed a wallet down on the table right under Bradley's nose and stood waiting for a reply. There was none. Bradley handed the wallet back to Turner and said something about it being time for emaciated old fools to stay at home and not interfere with things that didn't concern them.

The president came to the rescue by saying we would adjourn if there was no further official business to be taken care of.

When the meeting broke up, Bradley left in a huff, muttering darkly, but he said nothing directly to me. It was my general plan to undermine his position slowly and, when the time came, step in with a good hard push and get him out. I vaguely thought of this taking several weeks or months.

The Friday following this brush with Bradley, I went home about six in the evening. My apartment was a living room, bedroom, bath and kitchen in a large building near the business section of the city. I had taken it shortly after Adam Wilson had been exposed. I'd been a little shaky. There were several entrances to the building. The suite I selected was on the third floor, and had two entrances itself.

I opened the door and turned on the lights. There sat Bradley. Later I found the back door had been jimmied open.

CHAPTER 26

Fight

"WELL, wise guy," said Bradley, getting to his feet, "you and I have a little business to transact and we'll do it right now. I don't know what you're after, and I don't give a damn, but when you tried to hang a tag on me, you picked the wrong potato. Lodge 1536 ain't big enough for both of us. You're the one that's getting out and you're getting out tonight. I'll give you just one minute to write the lodge a letter, telling them you're leaving town to take a new job, or anything else you damn please. It's funny, but I really don't care much whether you write this letter or not. If you do, and I walk in and hand it to the secretary, the whole thing's over. If you don't write it, all I've got to do is get up in meeting and read the crowd some letters I found here. When I pass them around, you'll wish you was rotting away with old man Wilson. Well, skunk, which'll it be?"

The rank and file union men in Labor Day parades are not impressive, physically. But look at the presidents and other officers who ride in automobiles at the head of the column. Go to a labor-union convention and estimate the average weight of the delegates. These two hundred-pounders are not that way by chance. Somewhere along the line they needed every pound of that bone and muscle. I will not swear that they all used it in physical combat, but it was there if needed, and their smaller opponents knew it. Bradley had it. So did I.

As for the letters he had found—the little cupboard I had ingeniously installed in the tile front of the fireplace was open. I retained as few incriminating papers about the house as possible, but occasionally it was necessary. That morning I had cached two letters from the Chief in this secret place for further study. I must have left the door open, for he had not broken it.

A lot of things run through a man's mind when he is really up against it. Historians have remarked on the cowardice of mercenaries in battle. I was a paid fighter. On the other hand, Bradley was a free man, prepared to fight for his job, for his home, for his family, and his good name in the community. By this time, I was pretty sure he would fight, too. I had heard of his prowess as a bruiser when he was younger and making his way up in the labor movement. It was popularly supposed that he had settled down and had not engaged in physical battle for a good many years.

[171]

It suddenly seemed funny. I hadn't had a fight in fifteen years, not since I used to box at the Y. M. C. A. with the other kids. Suddenly Bradley looked like a kid in spite of his ferocious scowl. And I was another kid, and I suppose I was scowling and glaring too.

"How about it, rat? Your time is up."

"You wrote the ticket, brother," I said, "and I guess you're in for a ride." I recall that I did not raise my voice, but spoke softly and sadly. I was actually sorry, too. Regardless of how it was going to turn out, I wished men could find some other way to settle their differences. Who would care in ten or twenty or fifty years who had been boss of Electrical Workers' local 1536?

There was a table between us. Stepping backward one pace, I raised my foot to the edge of this table and shoved it over on Bradley with all my might. Right after the Adam Wilson affair I had become interested in some brass knuckles displayed in a pawn-shop window. I had bought a pair and carried one in each side trouser pocket. Before Bradley could get his balance after dodging the table I had donned the dusters, and was on top of him, swinging away with everything I had.

The fight was over in no time at all. Bradley lay unconscious, and the place was a shambles. My first blow cut a long gash in his forehead and the blood streamed into his eyes. This blinded him for a moment. I continued to plant blows on his face and kicks on his body until he went down, and out. My curiosity as to what a strong man could do with a set of pugilistic hardware was settled. I never saw a bloodier sight—even in the war. Knocking a man down is one thing. To keep on slugging a helpless mortal until he loses consciousness is something else. Bradley got up after the third knockdown, too weak to hold up his hands or defend himself. I had a real job forcing myself to knock him unconscious. When I did, I added a kick as he was falling. He hit the floor and lay with outstretched arms, dead to the world.

My letters were in his coat. To be on the safe side, I went through all his clothing and piled the contents of his pockets on the table. It was the usual collection of junk a man carries around, except for two bank books. One was a checking account deposit book on the First National. The other was on a savings bank. I thought they might have something to do with the union; but there was no reason the business agent should have union deposits in his own name; the treasurer handled all the union funds.

Bradley was still out; and he was still bleeding, but not fast enough for a severed artery. I tied his legs and arms and took several turns of rope around his head.

Then I studied the savings bank book. The balance was $6900, and the account had been started two years before. This meant deposits of $300 per month on an average. The First National book indicated deposits totaling $17,000 in about three years, or nearly $500 per month. Two items of $150 appeared every month in the First National book. This would be his pay from the local which was $300 monthly.

The other items varied considerably. Some months there were only the entries of his salary. In other months there would be as many as a dozen figures, all in even money from twenty-five dollars to several hundred. I looked in each book for the entries around the first of the year. Both showed big figures. Contractors got liberal at that time. Bradley still slept.

After gagging him I went into the bedroom where the phone was located.

"Do you know anything about Daniel L. Bradley?" I asked one of my friends when I got him on the wire. He was a brother in the clerks' union, and was employed at the First National Bank. He would have given me all the information in the secret files of the bank if I had wanted it. He promised to phone the teller who handled Bradley's account and call me back.

He called back in five minutes.

Bradley had carried an account for a long time. The daily balance averaged around $3,000. He had accounts with at least two brokers, and was always complaining about his bad luck in the stock market. He also claimed to be a consistent loser on the races. He was supposed to own two pieces of property valued at $12,000, clear and unencumbered. That was all they knew.

The figures as given in the books showed an average monthly income of $800. His salary was $300. It would seem the difference was not from successful speculation or gambling. And of course, he might have still other bank accounts. When I returned to the living room, Bradley's eyes were open but he was still too weak to move.

"You were saying we had some business together," I said in a death-sentence tone of voice, or as near to it as I could come. "You'll be glad to know it's all over. You gave me a choice of two things to do. I'm not taking either. I'm giving you only one choice, and you're going to take it. Right now I've got enough on you to send you to the pen for twenty years. When a guy gets $300 a month, and banks over a thousand, [an exaggeration in the light of all I knew at present] he's got something on his mind. Every district attorney and grand jury would like to know the details.

"You made some crack about having a couple of letters and you said something about old man Wilson. The last boot I gave you was on the old man's account. Now about those letters. I suppose you think you found them in that cupboard. Well, you didn't. Here's what happened. I came in and there were two guys with me. Not one, but two witnesses. We found you going through my desk. You showed fight. We took you on and as there were three of us, you got pretty well smeared. You didn't see any letters at all. If you still think you did, where are they? What's your word against three? Who's going to believe a guy who can't account for all the jack he's got in the bank?

"You said the local wasn't big enough for both of us. You're right, but you didn't go far enough. This town and the whole state isn't big enough. You're going to leave, and you're going to keep on going for a thousand miles. My crowd will see to it that you do. And another thing, don't think you can turn me up after you get away. If anything should happen to me, only one guy could have squealed. That's you. The bunch you'll meet then won't be easy on you as I've been.

"And, if anyone should happen to ask you who's boss of local 1536, send him to see me."

CHAPTER 27

To the Victor

I PHONED the garage where our Legion post kept the ambulance we had recently presented to the city. It was manned by a volunteer crew of Legionnaires, and was used mostly to take members, or their wives and families, to hospitals and home again.

I knew the man on duty, and I told him to bring the car and crew to my place. He was there in no time at all and we loaded Bradley in. I had taken off the ropes, but he knew better than to make any fuss. I had also phoned Burdette, the president of the electricians' local, and asked him to come to Union Hall right away and see that all the executive committee were there, on a matter of the greatest importance, well in advance of the regular meeting, which fortunately was scheduled for that night.

"Here's your ex-business agent," I said when the committee had gathered. "I want you to look over these books

[177]

and see whether you think this guy has been selling us out or not."

"Burdette," I said, getting him off to one side while the rest of the committee were going over the records, "I decided this guy was a crook a long time ago, and now I've proved it. So long as the committee knows this, I don't think it's any of their business just how I came to find it out, or how Bradley and I happened to tangle and end up here. Unless somebody insists on knowing, I'm saying nothing about it, and I don't think Bradley is going to say anything about it either."

"Oh, that's all right, I'm sure," Burdette said, all fluttery.

If Bradley demanded a show-down I was banking on the chief's getting a couple of men to swear they had been with me, and that we had found Bradley in my apartment. (My threat to Bradley that we would keep him in sight until he got away was based on the certainty that the Chief would assign a couple of men to shadow him until he moved on and got settled somewhere else.) But Bradley resigned, admitting everything. The boys decided not to prosecute if he would turn over every cent he owned, and all his property, to the lodge. I had half expected him to tell what he knew about me in spite of my threats, but he kept quiet, absolutely licked.

Then we had a talk about a successor as business agent and delegate to the Building Trades Council.

"There is only one sensible thing to do," Burdette finally said with conviction. "The brother who brought this disgraceful condition to light is the logical man for these positions. If he will take them I think we should make this recommendation to the lodge tonight, and have the appointments confirmed right away."

No, I couldn't take the office of business agent. It was a full-time job and I could not give it the time it demanded. I described the kind of man we needed, one who was not only honest, but who would take an active and intelligent interest in training our apprentices and raising the standards of our craft. I had several leads on such men, and would follow them up at once. The committee could count on the man I selected. Splendid. And would I accept election as delegate to the Building Trades Council? Yes, I would!

In two weeks the new business agent was installed. I felt pretty sure our office could tip me off to someone who would fill the bill, and they knew just the right man. He was a former business agent for a steel workers' local in another state. As a young man he had been an electrician, and he lost no time in brushing up his knowledge of the subject. His great asset, however, was that he knew the business agent's job thoroughly.

He was immediately popular with the rank and file members, who knew they could count on fair treatment. The contractors came to respect him also. He took favors from no one, assigned men in their regular order, and insisted that both sides live up to the letter of the contract. At the same time, he kept right after our members and insisted that they perfect themselves in their trade. His discipline in this respect was strict, and he would not hesitate to recommend lifting a member's card if there was a justifiable complaint against him from an employer.

Of course he did not know that his new boss was an operator.

The details of the Bradley affair were hushed up as much as possible, but I saw to it that a rumor persisted as to the identity of the man who had put him out. When he was able to leave the hospital, he and his wife and kids sneaked out of town. No one saw them go, and I didn't hear anyone speak with regret either.

When my monthly balance came from the home office, I found the Chief had given me the entire one-hundred-dollar raise, although Bradley had not been thrown out until the seventeenth.

The next time the executive committee met, Burdette took me to one side and asked if the nights the committee and the lodge met were satisfactory to me. He thought my other engagements might make a change in nights for the electricians' meetings more convenient. If I wished, he was sure he could oblige me. I got used to this in time.

The full details of this affair were never reported to my office; I tried but couldn't. I got stuck when I tried to write, "I then proceeded to knock hell out of this guy and didn't stop until he couldn't move his little finger." There were a lot of nice girls in this office, and they all liked me, and thought I was a fine fellow. I didn't want them to see anything like this.

I didn't want the Chief to see it either. He was always preaching that brain was the master of brawn, and we should put our stuff across by intellectual means alone. I used to wonder what he would have said if I had called him on the phone, saying, "Bradley's here in my room and I've either got to fight him, or resign from the union and take it on the lam." Years later, I told him all about it, and asked what he would have done if he had been in the same fix.

"It would never become necessary for me to decide what to do in a similar situation. I would have taken steps long before to avoid getting into such a predicament," he answered immediately. It gave me something to think about. What he meant was that he would have laid his plans so carefully that there could have been no possibility of having been taken by surprise.

CHAPTER 28

A Statue or Something

THE Building Trades Council met within a week after the electricians' lodge had elected me delegate to that august body. Most of the Council members were also delegates to the Central Labor Union and I was fairly well acquainted with them. The Building Trades Council president, a brick-layer named McGoorty, phoned me early on the day of the meeting with the request that I meet him sometime that afternoon. He was business agent for the bricklayer's local, and his time was largely his own. At my suggestion, I picked him up with my car several blocks away from Union Hall, where most of the locals had their headquarters.

"You and me can get together without any trouble," said McGoorty, apparently taking it for granted that I was as unscrupulous as the man I had displaced. I had driven to the outskirts of the city and we had chatted about the weather and current events. "Bradley and me ran the Council for the past few years, and you and I can do the same thing if you want to play ball. I'll be on the level with you and you can trust me. Just what are you after?"

"I ain't after much of anything, Mac," I replied without hesitation. "I've been a union man all my life, and although I haven't worked at my trade recently I still have a strong interest in union affairs. You asked me to come clean and I will. After the war I couldn't do shop work, so I took a whirl at the real-estate business. My first customers were union men, and I still get a lot of business from them. If it hadn't been for my union connections, I probably couldn't have started the Legion post. You are business man enough to know that I've made a lot of sales through my Legion connection. I've sold a good many houses during the past year, and between you and me the work that goes into these shacks is a disgrace. The bunch of dumbbells who belong to my local are as bad as any of the rest. There's no reason why the building trades mechanics of this town can't do as good work as anywhere else in the country, and I propose to make them do it."

I had stopped on the top of a little hill overlooking the river while talking. My last remark was delivered with considerable emphasis and I was looking him right in the eye. "And, Mac," I added significantly, "I wouldn't be at all surprised if the contractors of this town liked me and you so well after we develop some real building me-

[183]

canics that they erect a statue in our honor, or something."

Mac had not become boss of the bricklayers or elected president of the Building Trades Council because of any gross lack of intelligence.

"You and I are going to get along swell," he said extending his hand, which I took. "Nice view from up here. Wish we could stay and enjoy it all evening, but I guess we've both got plenty to do somewhere else."

There were no eyewitnesses to the trip Mac and I had made, and of course no one had been within earshot. A stenographic record of our conversation would have indicated nothing, even in a court of law. To a couple of experienced negotiators such as Mac and myself, however, it was clear that we had consummated a deal whereby peace and harmony would reign among the locals of our Building Trades Council for an indefinite time.

Meanwhile, we were to swing the big stick over the head of each Building Trades lodge until the caliber of work performed by the individual mechanic would pass the rigid tests we proposed. The building contractors and subcontractors were expected to be most appreciative. When that time arrived, it was tacitly agreed that these same contractors would be shaken down for a "statue in our honor or something." The shaking down was to be the sole function of Brother Mac and myself and the "something" would be subject to a fifty-fifty split between us.

The fact that Mac came to see me, instead of waiting for

me to call on him, was most significant. I had replaced Bradley in the electricians' lodge, but it did not necessarily follow that Mac would accept me as joint boss of the Building Trades Council in Bradley's place. Mac must have decided he would gain more by coming to me immediately with a proposition, than waiting and having a battle, and possibly losing everything. Sooner or later, he and I would fight it out for supreme control of the Building Trades group. This was a positive fact in my mind, and I assume it was in his. Until that time we would be on the level with each other and abide by the terms of our present partnership.

The Chief mildly criticized me for making a deal with McGoorty instead of going to the mat with him and striving for complete control of the council. Possibly I should have done so, but things had been moving so rapidly during the past few weeks that I honestly feared taking over the entire responsibility for the Building Trades Council, even if I could have got it. As time went on, I was able to convince the Chief, and he in turn was able to convince our contractor clients, that although I was not the president, or even titular boss, of the Building Trades Council, McGoorty, the elected head, was unable to do anything without my approval. After they had seen proof of this they readily agreed that the situation was excellent.

I never saw such a dumbfounded group of men as the contractors when they began to realize that the building mechanics were getting real instruction in their trades. During

[185]

the next few months at least one hundred men, including several with years of experience, were suspended from various lodges and made to serve another apprenticeship. To stimulate interest in the building trades I gave numerous lectures at high schools, Boy Scout troop meetings, and young men's clubs. All this made a good impression on the public, and I am convinced that a lot of fine young men decided to learn a trade as a result.

Added to those I already had, these new responsibilities kept me very busy. My labor offices included: recording secretary and CLU delegate from the Clerks' Union; vice president, executive committee-man, chairman of the organizing committee, and Building Trades Council delegate from the Electricians'; chairman of the newly formed trade improvement committee of the Building Trades Council (my office of co-boss of this body was unofficial but nevertheless effective); member of the organizing committee, and chairman of the entertainment committee of the Central Labor Union.

In addition to these union offices, I was commander of the Union Post of the American Legion and a member of several civic committees to which I had been appointed by the mayor to represent the American Legion.

Almost every night in the week I attended at least one meeting. These were usually preceded by a dinner for the principal officers of the various associations. Luncheons with business or fraternal groups were also a daily occurrence. My real-estate business suffered considerably, and it was fortunate that my salary had been raised in proportion to my increased labor activities—although, remembering what happened to GF-14, I made a point of impressing my labor friends with the fact that the real-estate business was booming.

CHAPTER 29

Shop Talk

FOR a while on the Centerville assignment, I had submitted daily reports just as I had done while working in one of the shops. As I became busier, with a meeting nearly every night, this proved impossible, and reports were submitted every other day. Still later the reports were reduced to two a week, and finally a weekly résumé was all that was asked of me, although I of course forwarded a bit of hot news whenever it came up.

I mailed the résumé on Sunday. Our office received it on Monday. It was edited to correct spelling and grammatical errors, and then compared carefully with the daily reports sent in by operators in Centerville shops. This was important as I saw things from a different angle than the shop men, and although two of us might report the same incident truthfully our reports would not always agree as to details.

[188]

For example, in one of my reports I said the molders' local had received application for membership from two men employed in a certain foundry. One of our operators was a member of this local and he swore, when queried, that no such applications had been received. In this instance I was right. The official who secured the applications was holding them back while he made an effort to enlist all the men in the shop. He told me, as a personal friend in the labor movement, but he had not told even the other officers of his own local, much less the ordinary members.

My report was then typed in duplicate and one copy was mailed to the secretary of the Centerville Manufacturers Association at his home address. Excerpts were also made of those sections of my report that mentioned specific shops, or one of our clients, or a specific industry. The secretary of the manufacturers' association handed these excerpts to the officers of the companies concerned as soon as he received them. At a weekly meeting of the directors of the association, the secretary read my report in its entirety.

Although this secretary knew my identity, every effort was made to preserve my anonymity among the officers and members of the association. I often met our clients at civic or social gatherings and I used to wonder if any of them ever suspected that I, the well-known real-estate broker and labor leader, was in their employ.

On an assignment of this sort it was not necessary to render such detailed reports as it had been for shop work. I was known to be a reliable and experienced operator and my word was taken for a lot of things on which I formerly had had to write pages. For instance, I might state that there was no organizing activity on the part of the stationary firemen's union. I did not have to tell that I had obtained this information while spending several hours with one of the union's officers trying to sell him a vacant lot, and that he had told me what was going on in his lodge. If it had been necessary for me to report all the conversations I had with labor leaders each week, a dozen secretaries would have been needed. It was bad enough as it was and I think anyone will agree after reading this typical report.

GT-99
Report for week ending Aug. 6.
Meetings:
Central Labor Union: Regular monthly meeting held August 2, in Union Hall.
All lodges represented except musicians.
All officers present.
Visitors: Grand Lodge Representative Carlson of Printers' Union.
Regular order of business: Nothing of interest until:
Organizing Committee: Chairman Clancy reported one member of the Committee (GT-99) had visited eleven local unions at their invitation during the past month and talked along general organizing lines and called particular attention to Union Post of the American Legion which is now being formed by and for union men. This post is holding a smoker which is open to all ex-service men in Union Hall on August 1. All union veterans and their friends are invited.

New Business: The chair announced the Labor
Day Parade last year had only 311 marching men
and this was a disgrace to the labor movement of
Centerville. Absolutely no interest in parade. It
died without any help from me. If 50% of each
lodge will parade, it's on; otherwise not.

Good of the Order: Rand (Molders) announced
that organizer B. F. Smith of the Molders' International would be in the city all of next month
in interests of molders at Compact Stove Co. The
CLU secretary was instructed by the chair to
write a letter to Brother Smith, offering the facilities of the CLU and Union Hall to assist him in
his work.

Ralston (Plasterers) arrived pretty well loaded and
had to be called down by the chair several times
for talking all over the place. Finally he got into an
argument with Dodge (Carpenters) about their
old feud regarding erection of metal lathe. Ralston
called Dodge a "Laborskate" and we had to pull
them apart when Dodge started to take a poke at
him. Weaver (Truckmen) asked Ralston what a
"laborskate" was and the reply is a classic. "A
laborskate," said Ralston, "is a bozo who shoots
off his bazoo all the time about something he don't
know nothing about." This got a big laugh and
there was no more fighting.

Carlson, grand lodge organizer for the printers,
asked for the floor. He reported the agreement
he has been negotiating for the past three weeks
with the daily papers in behalf of the printers would
be signed tomorrow. He said it would run for
three years with a sliding scale of wages depending
on cost of living. He praised attitude of newspaper
officials and expressed hope day would come when

[191]

all trades could agree as amicably.

Adjournment: At 9:15 P. M. so members could attend boxing bouts at Elks Hall.

After meeting, Weaver (Truckmen) told his friends he now had signed applications from all the drivers at the Boston Store and the Empire City Ice Cream Co. He claims that as busses replace the trolleys and the interurban lines he is going after the bus drivers and keep them out of the streetcar local. It is understood that the truckmen (International Association of Teamsters, Chauffeurs, Stablemen and Helpers) have no jurisdiction over bus drivers employed by a public utility but Weaver won't let this stop him. The old men who now run the trolleys will probably be laid off as the busses arrive and younger men will be hired. (CHI, for the love of Mike, get someone into this union to slow things up. Weaver is my good friend but I can't do a darn thing from this end. What it needs is a real obstructionist working inside. How's that for a good word?)

After the fights at the Elks, most of the CLU members hung around the bar until it closed at 1:00 A. M. No hard liquor but plenty of beer. This is shipped from somewhere across the river every Thursday and it arrives at the club about 4:00 A. M. Friday. (Some of Weaver's truckmen are supposed to run it in. Do you want any dope on this?)

No talk of organizing or other activity of interest during the bar session.

Electricians' Local: Regular monthly business meeting held on August 4, in Union Hall.

All officers present except Treasurer Nolte who is working nights this week.

31 members present.

Visitors, none.

Regular order of Business: Nothing of note until:
   Report of Treasurer: Cash in bank and Liberty bonds $14,311.46. This is probably the best union balance in the city next to the printers who are supposed to have about $30,000 in their war chest.
   Organizing Committee: Reported applications from both electricians employed regularly at the Agnew Shovel works. Names are L. C. Snow and F. M. Murphy.
   Good of the Order: Decided not to make a definite promise regarding participation in Labor Day parade.
   Adjournment: At 8:40 P. M. The meeting took just 20 minutes from the time it was called to order.

Miscellaneous Activity:

I attended and spoke at a meeting of the Barbers' Local on the evening of August 3. They are doing a good deal of organizing but I guess nobody cares except the master barbers. This is a fine crowd of men, 107 present at the meeting. They are mostly of Italian birth or parentage. One fellow named Calabrese was an aviator in the Italian army during war and a prisoner in Austria for a year. After I made my Legion speech, he rose and said he would join if we would accept him and he would bring not less than 25 men with him who had served in either the Italian or American Army. At first this didn't seem like such a good idea as I was hoping to keep this Legion post pretty much Americanized but it suddenly dawned on me that the bigger the mixture of races and nationalities and the larger the post, the less attention will be paid to the union angle. I have decided to soft pedal the union idea as much as possible from now on.

[193]

A visit was made to the machinists' lodge to give my Legion speech on August 5. They had only 26 members present and the president apologized profusely for the small turn-out. Nothing of interest learned while there. I drove two members home who were going my way. One is named Shannon and he said he had just started to work last week at the Milton Hosiery Mills. There are four other machinists employed there. The plant has a very complete little machine shop, where it repairs all its machinery and makes a good many of the simpler replacement parts. None of the other machinists are union men. Shannon says he has been talking unionism to the other boys and they are interested. This is a new plant and most of the employees who work on the stocking machines came here from around Philadelphia and Reading, Penn. where there are a lot of knitting mills and they are all unionized. I think there is a regular hosiery workers' union which is affiliated with the United Textile Workers. The Textile Workers are suspected of being slightly left-wing and I seem to have heard the hosiery workers are the most radical of the bunch. I'll smell around this place in a day or two and learn what I can. (Yes, I know, I'll do my darnedest to get enough dope so that we can sell the boss of the shop on placing a *man* there—but at least half the force are women.)

The three men fired from the Collins Lumber Company for joining the teamsters' union have all obtained employment. Brady is driving a truck for the Centerville Builders' Supply Co. Nelson is with the city as a paving inspector which job was procured for him by his brother who is ward captain of the 5th ward. Seagrave is driving for the Rossiter Laundry and Dry Cleaning Company. I do not know whether they have resigned from the union or not but will find out this week when I have a chance to talk with Weaver.

No travelling labor leaders passed through this week.

Here's one I got from Durkee of the mail carrier's the other day. He had just returned from a visit to his old home in Ireland and had gone over to London for a few days. "After looking at the queen," says Durkee, "I can understand why the English sing, 'God Save the King.'"

And now that the city has been saved for another week, I'm going out to Old Maryville and go in swimming without any laborites around to mar the scenery.

Yours,
GT-99.

Essentially, this report differs but little from thousands received in our office. Of course the wisecracks and facetious comments would be edited out before the report went to the client, but the office men enjoyed them.

CHAPTER 30

On to the Capital

As soon as the new electrical workers' business agent was installed I went to the State Capital to get acquainted with the president of the State Federation of Labor, as the Chief had suggested at the conclusion of the linesmen strike.

It was surprising how fast things moved. The Chief had spoken truly in saying that anyone with four hundred votes in his pocket was a power to be reckoned with in any man's country.

There were a couple of things on my mind besides meeting the president of the State Federation. Our Legion Post had recently received a letter from the adjutant general of the state asking us to assist in the formation of one or more units of the National Guard, as the old National Guard had been disbanded after the armistice and there was now a demand to have it revived.

Two classes of people are interested in working for a

strong National Guard—the manufacturers, as represented by Chambers of Commerce and other trade associations, and the men who hold commissions in the Guard. As soon as a strike situation gets beyond the control of local police authority the governor is asked to send the National Guard to preserve order. In reality preserving order means simply the protection of property, and the property to be protected is always plants and equipment owned by the corporation whose employees are on strike. It is cheaper for an employer to receive protection from a few companies of National Guardsmen than for him to hire several hundred private guards, which he would have to pay and maintain out of his own pocket. Many Chambers of Commerce make direct cash contributions to guard units in their cities and the reason for their liberality is obvious.

Our Centerville clients were anxious to have a few companies of militia in the city, and, as my army experience in some measure qualified me for the task, the chief suggested that I look into the matter of organizing them. Most men of military age had a strange distaste for the army and army matters in the years immediately following the war, but nevertheless the national spirit still ran high. Union men were no exception to the general rule. The National Guard had never been called out for a strike in this part of the country, and union leaders offered no objection when I became identified with it. Construction of an armory, which would give work to union craftsmen, also favorably impressed the labor element.

It was natural to expect the Veterans' organizations to sponsor a move to revive the guard, and the Legion Post had discussed the matter with interest. Our section of the state was predominantly industrial. The adjutant general hoped we could recruit men with machine shop experience, as they would be excellent material for the engineers' regiment. I had already talked to the personnel directors of the largest factories and found them enthusiastic. They agreed to grant two weeks' vacation with pay to all men who enlisted. This meant that a man in the National Guard would get his vacation during the summer at the time the regiment went to camp for the required field training period. If he were paid his full salary by his employer during his absence, the proposition would be more appealing than if the man got only his National Guard pay of something like a dollar a day. I was sure I could enlist one or more companies and therefore had a definite program to propose to the adjutant general.

I also wanted to meet the commissioner of Banks and Banking. Savings and loan companies were springing up on all sides because of the enormous boom in home construction. I could see no reason why such a bank, with labor-union backing, should not be inaugurated in our town. The small amount of study I had given to the question seemed to indicate that these banks were easily formed, and that only a nominal capital was required. Although I was not anxious to be the president, or to operate such a bank myself, I was sure it would enhance my prestige as a union man if it became known that I was the principal sponsor.

My first call was at the office of the adjutant general. He had been a politician at the other end of the state for many years and had been active in the former National Guard. During the war he had been advanced to the rank of colonel. His political and military record, augmented by his support of the victorious state ticket in the last election, had brought him his present appointment. He received me with open arms.

Due to the distaste of American youth for all things military in those days the formation of National Guard units was meeting opposition. I walked in with the promise of at least one company, and possibly a whole battalion.

During the next three days, the adjutant general and I had several discussions, and he promised that I should be captain of the new company, and that I could select my other officers and recruit my men without interference from him. It was also agreed that if I could raise an entire battalion, I should be the major to command it.

The most pleasing aspect of my interviews with the general, as well as with the other politicians, was that they all seemed to have information to the effect that I swung considerable weight in my home town. The fact that the section of the state in which I resided was of a different political faith from that of the party in power undoubtedly had much to do with this. So far I had kept out of Centerville politics and hadn't announced any party affiliation. A state election would be held the coming November. Hence

[199]

I could not have picked a better time for my visit, for the politicians were angling for my support.

When I told the adjutant general that it was my intention to make the acquaintance of the banking department he immediately arranged an appointment, and insisted on accompanying me to make the introductions. I encountered the same consideration at the hands of the people in charge of this bureau. The banking department gave me a complete outline as to how to form a savings and loan company. The commissioner readily agreed to come to our town and help us get started as soon as I got my directors together. He would be glad to confer with us, assist in preparing our application for a charter, and would even lend us an assistant from his office for a couple of weeks during our organization period.

My interest in these contacts had been so great that I did not get to see Mr. Allen, the president of the State Federation of Labor, until the fourth day. The underground telegraph had been in operation, and when I walked into his office he already knew of my presence in the city, and expressed regret that I had not called to see him sooner.

Allen was a carpenter by trade. He had been successively president and business agent of his own local, and then president of the State Council of Carpenters. He had secured his present office some three years ago, and was solidly entrenched in it. He was also a politician, and held an appointment under the governor in the department of Public Buildings. This position required him to make frequent inspection trips throughout the state, and he utilized these visits to keep in touch with labor organizations. I learned later that he did a little electioneering for his party at the same time.

He was an affable handshaker, not only delighted to make my acquaintance, but willing to promise anything I might wish in the way of political favors. The union men of my town had not supported him at the last state convention.

When I returned to Centerville I found a note from Irving Gerber, the local chairman of the political party to which my state capital friends belonged. He was an attorney whom I had met several times at civic gatherings. To my surprise, he knew all about my visit to the capital, and intimated that he would like to offer his assistance with any of the projects I had in mind. He asked numerous leading questions, obviously hoping that I would indicate my political preferences. Instinct warned me to remain noncommittal. I wished to consult the Chief before going any further.

The late great Samuel Gompers announced the political program of labor unions many years ago when he said, "Labor's votes will be used to reward its friends and punish its enemies." This meant that every labor organization affiliated with the American Federation of Labor could determine its own political policy and support whomever it chose. In political years, every local union, central labor union, and State Federation of Labor approved a lengthy list of candidates. These lists generally included names from all political parties. The principal requirement was that the individual candidate should have been friendly to labor in the past.

All politicians ardently woo the labor vote; so it is not uncommon to find every candidate of every party given a sweeping endorsement. As a result, the labor vote in those days was scattered to the winds. Our state and city were no exception in this regard, and this explains the interest our local political leaders soon manifested in me.

As soon as possible I had a talk with the Chief about the political situation. He decided that I should retain a position of strict neutrality, and follow to the letter the advice of Gompers about "rewarding and punishing." In the end this was proved the wiser course as it had the rival parties bidding for my support.

This story is about labor, not about political parties or a political campaign. I have touched on how contacts between politicians and labor leaders are made. So far as I could learn, they differ little from the contacts the same politicians made with church groups, women's clubs, granges, bar associations and fraternal orders.

CHAPTER 31

I Meet Mike

THE convention of the State Federation of Labor was scheduled for August. It was to be held in the legislative chambers of the state capital. The governor received credit for being most gracious to organized labor by offering the state house, although this was merely good business. Our state had an unusually large number of labor voters.

I had to decide which of my various organizations I would represent as a delegate. There would be little prestige in going to the state convention as a delegate from the retail clerks' union, so I passed that up. I then decided it might hurt my standing with the electricians to insist on becoming the delegate from that body, so I let some of the old-timers of that lodge be elected to represent it. Bradley, our former business agent, usually attended state conventions as a delegate from the Building Trades Council, where he had been the electricians' representative. Since I had taken over most of his other duties, I concluded it would be best to attend the state convention as a delegate from the Building Trades, just as he had done.

"Sure thing," was McGoorty's instant response when I announced my decision to him. "You and me are running the show and we will go to the convention together. We might get a couple of rooms side by side, and then you can keep your eye on me."

The state capital was only four hours away by automobile. In my car I took McGoorty, President Broderick of the Central Labor Union, and a barber named Brophy. Brophy and Broderick were buddies, and were the delegates from the Central Labor Union. The four of us were the acknowledged leaders of union labor in Centerville.

Never have I known three men with better dispositions or men who appreciated a holiday more than McGoorty, Broderick and Brophy. They shouted and sang all the way to the capital. We got a suite—two bedrooms with a living-room between. I shared a room with McGoorty, while Broderick and Brophy had the other.

The day we arrived I heard a man playing the piano on the mezzanine above the hotel lobby. He was a big fat fellow. I don't remember ever hearing anyone, before or since, who could get so much out of a piano. In the evening, just before dinner, I heard him playing again. I got my banjo, and walked up to the mezzanine from the lobby, singing and playing as I went. He was rendering "Madelon" with a little more ad lib than I had thought possible.

I sang the song in English, and then in French, and then we tore into most everything in the current folio. He would finish one number and then run it right into another without a break. At first I had a good deal of trouble following, as I played only by ear and he was constantly changing keys. He noticed my difficulty, however, and after that as soon as he started a new piece he would announce the key loudly enough for me to hear. Finally we came to a rousing finish with "Mademoiselle from Armentiers." There were at least two hundred people in the lobby, union delegates and other guests, and we got a real ovation when our concert ended.

The pianist arose from his seat, held out his hand, and said, "My name is Michaels, and I'm the business agent of the electricians' union in Fayette. Come on in to dinner with my bunch, and afterwards we'll challenge these stuck-up musicians' delegates to a jazz tournament and win all their dough. Brother, I'm sure glad to meet you."

I laughed and introduced myself. This was the start of a friendship that lasted for many years. In addition to being business agent for his local, Michaels was a delegate to the Building Trades Council, the C. L. U., and a city council-man. In fact he had his finger in almost everything that went on in his part of the state. Also he was a strong sup-porter of Allen, the president of the State Federation of Labor; and politically their views were the same. Michaels was just the sort of man I had hoped to meet.

The convention did not open officially until the follow-ing day, but there were at least one hundred of the boys already in town and most of them had dinner in the hotel where we were staying. There was a smoker in the ballroom that evening. Not by request, but by demand, Michaels and I had to stop in the middle of our dinner and play for the crowd. At the smoker we did the same thing. My old banjo had cost only $35 when I bought it some ten years earlier, but as a means of getting acquainted it proved to be worth many times that sum to me.

At the smoker I knocked off playing long enough to tell the crowd a few stories. The next day I rehearsed Michaels in a few of them so that we could put them across together. This helped the act. Mike (as Michaels was known to almost every man there) had been literally aching to find a playmate, and I was the boy for him. He drank as little as I and seemed to rely on his abundance of animal spirits to keep him going.

My first state labor convention was exactly like dozens of other labor meetings I have attended. It opened with a prayer, followed by an address of welcome from the president of the local Central Labor Union. He introduced the governor of the state and the mayor of the city. The president of the State Federation then gave his report and introduced the presidents of four international labor unions. Everyone made a speech. Everyone was applauded. Everyone was bored.

A host of committees were then appointed to take care of resolutions, organization, grievances, boycotts, union labels, safety, good of the order, nominations, legislation, credentials, time and place of the next convention, and probably a lot of other things that I have forgotten.

Proposals on every conceivable subject were introduced from the floor, and promptly referred by the chair to these committees. This was followed by another outburst of oratory that lasted for a day. Committees then started to report, and almost without exception their reports were adopted as read.

The only item of business in which I was particularly interested was the selection of the city in which the next state convention would be held. I had decided to bring it to Centerville and could already picture myself as one of the official hosts.

I told McGoorty my plans and he readily agreed. I therefore left the matter in his hands, and he entertained the committee proper in our suite, with the able assistance of Broderick, Brophy and myself. My three associates set up the drinks, and led the way in consuming them. I played the banjo and led the harmonizing. When the party was over, the committee would have insisted on the North Pole as a convention site if my gang of Centerville delegates had suggested it. (Needless to say, the Chief's clients eventually paid my share of the cost of this party.)

I also did a little trading with my piano-playing friend, Mike, in arranging the next convention. Each day we had entertained the delegates with our music, and although we were the best of friends, we had not spoken a word about our connection with the union movement. I asked Mike to take a ride in my car on the afternoon of the third day. It would also give me a chance to look at a piece of farm property on the outskirts of the city that one of my Centerville clients owned and wished to dispose of.

"From all I hear," I said to Mike when we got under way, "you've got a good deal to say about what goes on in your part of the state. Before this party breaks up let's talk things over and see if we can't help each other out a little. I'm here to say that no matter what happens I'm not going to fight with you about anything in the world. You say you've been looking for a partner for your musical act for a long time. I have, too. The whole union business can go to hell before I'll take a chance on losing out on this duet. If you don't think we can get along together in business, we'll stop right now and stick to our music."

"That's just about the way I feel about it," he replied. "I've been in the labor racket longer than you have, but I won't claim to know any more about it, for you seem to have done pretty well by yourself. Someday I'd like to hear your version of the Bradley affair. I knew him pretty well, but we never talked the same language. I'll come clean on my line-up in Fayette. In another three or four years I can run the town if I can get the reformers back of me and then keep them interested; and incidentally I'll have done something no one else ever has been able to do.

"No, I don't want to be mayor. Our town isn't quite the kind that will stand for a union man in the mayor's office. We're figuring on putting on a commission form of government, and if I can get to be one of the five commissioners you can bet the rest of the bunch will have a tough time getting away with anything. That's what I'm after. There's not so much money in running an honest government as in running a crooked one like the one we've had down there for years, but I don't do so badly. What's your set-up?"

I told Mike about my real-estate connection, which I had built up with union backing, and also about the Union Savings and Loan Association (Mike made a note of this and thought he might try it himself). I admitted using my union connections to further my private business. I also found it impossible to be connected with anything and not try to run it.

This accounted for my activity in the electrical workers' local and the central trade bodies. In other words, Mike and I described ourselves as being in much the same situation. The labor movement to both of us was secondary to our ambitions in other directions.

"I want you to come down and visit me this fall," Mike said, as we were driving back to town. "We've got some of the best hunting in the country in our part of the state, and I always knock off for a few days and go out with a crowd you'll like.

"There's another thing on my mind too. You had a linemen's strike up your way, and it lost out pretty badly. The electrical local I belong to is just like yours, all building trades electricians. Then, we have a linemen's local also. This linemen's bunch lost a strike about fifteen years ago and the old timers who still carry cards are hoping to get even with the company. There are about twenty in the local, just enough to keep the charter, and they haven't done much for years except meet and crab about how much they hate the outfit they work for. I act as business agent for this local too. In the last couple of months your friend Hinds has dropped in several times. Last week he was there and I had a long talk with him. He thinks the chances of organizing the linemen are excellent—both the ones who work for the light company and the street-car company—and I agree with him.

"We've got a peculiar situation down there. The main lines in our part of the state are over pretty hilly country, and even the ordinary lines are in some pretty bad spots. I honestly don't think the company could bring a lot of strike-breakers in there who could take the work over as they did in Centerville. Neither the light company nor the street-railway company is part of a big trust, such as you had to contend with. This means they won't be able to rush in a bunch of skilled strike-breakers from other companies.

"Bear in mind I'm not advocating a strike, and I'm the last person in the world who wants one. I never saw one yet where the men didn't lose, even if they won, and you know what I mean. But here's the situation. These companies treat the men like dogs and haven't increased wages a penny since the war. They've got some seniority rules, but they don't pay any attention to them.

"The street-car conductors have a local, but it's always been afraid of its own shadow. Recently I've been putting some pep into it. By the time Hinds has the linemen organized, I'm going to have this bunch of conductors hardened up so they can bite right through nails.

"Now, here's what I have in mind for you to do, and if you do it you can count on me reciprocating—any time. You were through one of these strikes and should know a little about it. You can talk and make yourself agreeable. I'd like to have you drop in several times this fall and give me a hand at some of our rallies, and also give me your advice on things."

Ho hum! So that's what my good-natured musical friend was up to. Sure I could help him. Any time at all, just say the word and I would come running. Meanwhile, all I wanted was his support in getting the convention for Centerville next year.

"Fellow, leave it to me," said Mike enthusiastically. "I was thinking of taking it to Fayette, but you can have it and welcome. When the committee reports on the floor I'll withdraw in your favor. You're probably working on the committee and I'll help you there if you want me to.

"Now how about these officers of the State Federation? I've been plugging for Allen for president again, and I think he should get it for the main reason that it'll take a real fight to get him out. I had a talk with him last night, and he promised that if he can be president one more year, he'll step out and throw the job up for grabs. Next year, you and I will be used to working together and we'll figure this out to suit ourselves. How about it?"

I agreed. In fact, neither Mike nor I could bring up a single thing we didn't agree on. We were young and the future looked most inviting, with the pair of us dividing the labor spoils of the state.

The convention agreed, without debate, to come to Centerville for the next meeting, and President Allen appointed me chairman of the convention committee. The other members were CLU presidents from the leading cities, who held these appointments by courtesy only, and had nothing at all to do with the actual planning of the convention.

I had accomplished all the objectives specified by my Chief, including getting acquainted with some of the real leaders of the American labor movement, a few of whom had attended our state convention. I had made a good impression on them by going to them for advice on various local problems. As a rule, nothing is more ingratiating than to ask a man to give you some advice. Fortunately there is no law requiring one to follow it.

CHAPTER 32

A Friendly Visit with Mike

A FEW days after the state convention the Chief asked me to come to the main office for a general discussion of the situation in Centerville, as well as to talk over plans for the future.

I had told the Chief all about my acquaintance with Michaels, the piano-playing business agent of the Fayette electricians' local. "Attaboy!" he chortled. "I've been trying to do business with both the street-car company and light and power people in Fayette for years. I want you to go down there about the time Hinds arrives and starts organizing. I'll have him watched and tell you when. Tell your friend Mike you were taking a little motor trip, and drop in on him without announcing yourself. I don't want this to be a formal visit in response to his invitation as you'll want to go back later. What I want is exact information as to where Hinds is staying and all about him. I want

[213]

to be able to walk in on the light and street-car company people and give them a lot of facts they can check up on if they want to. I've got an idea we can make a lot of money out of this, and we won't have to use a single operator, and there won't be a strike or anything like it."

About three weeks later the Chief called me on the phone and said Hinds had arrived in Fayette that day and was registered at the Empire Hotel under the name of Hanson. The Chief had assigned a man to trail him and this was his final report. I got to Fayette the following day about noon.

Michaels was standing in front of the Labor Temple with a couple of other men when I drove along the main street. I hailed him and got the welcome of my life. He dragged me right up to his office, and then out to his house for lunch. I liked his wife immediately. It seems that he'd told her about meeting me at the convention, and from the moment I entered their door, neither of them could do enough for me. I had my banjo in the car, and we had to have a concert right away, to the delight of Mrs. Mike and at least a dozen neighbors she called in.

I told Mike I hadn't intended to stop as I'd been away on a business trip and was two days late in getting back to Centerville. I'd happened to see him on the street and I couldn't resist the temptation to say, "Hello," but I must get under way immediately. I had to be home for a Building Trades Council meeting that night.

"Listen to me, you lowdown crooner," said Mike to the accompaniment of a mighty slap on the back, "what you say doesn't mean anything to me or anyone else in my town. You're here and you're going to stay here for three separate and distinct reasons. In the first place, the city council has a meeting tonight, and after it's over we're having a party for our chief of police who is resigning after forty years of service. The old boy is really getting laid on the shelf, but we're making it as nice for him as we can. You've got to go to the party and meet this bunch. Then we're going to give them some music they'll remember all their lives. Hell, all I've done since I got back from the convention is brag about you. If you try to run out on me like this, I'll just have you locked in the klink and that's all there is to it.

"And in the second place," he said, looking furtively about, "Hinds got here yesterday and is starting to work today. I'm going to meet him this afternoon at three o'clock and I want you to come with me. He'll be glad to see you. I told him you might come down to help out.

"And in the third place, you long-legged, slab-sided so-and-so, you've got to stay for at least a day so I can show you off to the missus. All she's done since the convention is listen to me talk about the good time I had there, and what a swell guy you are. Honest, you've got to stick around to let me show her I know what I'm talking about."

I made a big show of phoning McGoorty and telling him I was detained in Fayette and would have to miss the meeting that night. I did this from Mike's home. He heard the conversation and it all sounded good. We chatted a while longer and went downtown to see Hinds.

[215]

"How do you fellows like these cookies?" Hinds asked, pulling several papers out of his pocket and tossing them onto the table after we had exchanged greetings. The "cookies" were signed applications for membership in the electricians' union from seven employees of the electric light company. I can see the names yet; Eagle, Shute, Bronson, Hathaway, Brown, Sneddon and Thatcher. I repeated them to myself a hundred times as we talked. At that stage of the game I could remember at least twenty names without making a mistake, and had often done so; but I knew I mustn't slip on these. I figured that each of them meant at least a hundred dollars to me in commissions if the chief was able to put his deal across.

"Brother Hinds," I said taking his hand, "I'm a lucky man to have dropped in today and be privileged to see the start of a campaign to liberate these hundreds of unfortunate men."

We stayed with Hinds only a short time, and then went to the City Hall, where Mike introduced me to a host of his friends and associates. Every city councilman is popular on account of his position, but there was no doubt that Mike was loved by these people for a deeper and more sincere reason. And here was his friend, the great friend of whom he had spoken so often in the past few weeks.

I got to thinking about what I would do with Mike when he came to Centerville. I could introduce him to as many important people. My friends would put themselves out for him, just as his were doing for me; but there was a difference. I couldn't put my finger on it right then, but finally I got it. If I were turned up, or the job were canceled, or I decided to quit, I could walk away from Centerville without once looking back. To have taken Mike away from his town would have been like tearing him away from his wife. His heart was there, and his work showed it. He was building a monument. I was working for a salary and commission.

The first opportunity I got I ducked in to a pay station and called the Chief's secretary, giving her the names of the seven light and power men who had made application for union membership. She told me the Chief was away but for me to call him again before noon the following day as he might have some instructions.

The farewell affair for the chief of police was held in the Elks' ballroom. The mayor and numerous other dignitaries made brief remarks commenting on the splendid career of the old gentleman while a servant of the city. The recorder of deeds then stepped up to the chief's wife and handed her the deed to a house and lot as a gift from the city employees. The old couple were so overcome with emotion that neither was able to say a single word in reply.

In the meantime, Mike and I had stationed ourselves at the piano. We played for almost an hour. I never saw a man enjoy himself more than Mike did. Afterwards, he introduced me to almost every man, woman and child at the party, and his presentation was invariably such that there was no doubt of how I stood with him.

On one occasion he led me across the room and presented me to a short, stocky middle-aged man named Paulson. "Brother Paulson is an international organizer for the Textile Workers," he said. "He blew into town a few days ago and is looking over the situation at the textile mills here, and we hope to prevail on him to hang around long enough to start a local. I've got to join the committee and escort the chief of police out to this new home of his, but I'll be back in less than an hour. You two fellows will find a lot to talk about."

"So you're from Centerville," remarked Paulson, as soon as I had explained my union connection. "I'm going up there in a few days and look over the hosiery mills in your town. The hosiery workers are a division of our union and, although I don't do any organizing for them, I get as much information on their line as I can. Textile workers are treated worse than those in almost any other trade, and it's no job at all to get them into a union."

He told me about the weaving mills in Fayette, and said he was going to report to his headquarters that the time was ripe to organize them and he hoped to get permission to do so. He then inquired about what I thought of the situation in the hosiery plants in Centerville. I told him about the two disastrous union experiences in that city during the past couple of years, and strongly advised against making any organizing effort for another year at least. I was sure he would incur considerable opposition, and if it was as easy to organize the textile hands as he claimed it to be, I was sure he could do better with less effort elsewhere. He thanked me for my advice and said it was information of this sort he was trying to get.

I gave him my card and told him to look me up when he reached Centerville, and that I would be glad to introduce him to the labor leaders of the city and drive him around in my car so he could see the mills. Paulson readily accepted my invitation, provided he came there. He knew the folly of trying to organize in towns where strikes had been lost recently. He never came. A few words from me at this chance meeting had done the work.

Mike insisted on my spending the night at his home. I said I would have to leave shortly after daybreak. He and his wife were up early and she prepared a splendid breakfast before I started. I drove away with their invitation to return ringing in my ears. Although I was a welcome guest in the homes of several hundred people in Centerville I knew of no place in the entire world where my welcome was as sincere as in the home of these good friends. I promised to come back for a few days of hunting later in the fall, and invited my host and hostess to visit me.

CHAPTER 33

Bread-and-Butter Letter

ALTHOUGH it was not yet seven o'clock in the morning I phoned the Chief from a pay station in an all-night restaurant. He was wide-awake, and instructed me to meet him in a town about one hundred miles from Fayette that afternoon. He would be in the hotel under an assumed name, and he told me to use some name other than my own when I asked for him.

The Chief had a longer distance to come, and he did not make his appearance until about four o'clock. He asked me to tell him everything I had found out about the organizing work of brother Hinds among the linemen in Fayette.

"The president of the light and power company and his attorney are here in the hotel right now," the Chief said, when I had finished. "Yesterday I called the president on the phone and tried to make an appointment, but he refused. So I called the president of the Centerville

Light & Power Company, and got him to telephone the Fayette power people and convince them that it was to their interest to see me. This made an impression, and the president of the Fayette power company phoned me within an hour. I suggested meeting here so that no one in Fayette would have the slightest chance of finding out what's going on. The reason I want you here is that I may call you in during the conference. If I call you, all you'll have to do is tell them just what you told me and answer any questions they ask."

At the end of an hour no call had come from the Chief; so I decided to take a nap and catch up on the sleep I had missed the night before. I was awakened by the telephone ringing. The Chief wanted me to come to his suite. It was eight o'clock.

I was presented to the president of the power company and his attorney. Neither shook hands, each giving me a curt nod to acknowledge the introduction. The Chief told me to relate the story as I knew it. I did, leaving out my connection with Mike, and merely telling of my conversation with Hinds, and that I had actually seen seven signed applications from the men I named. It was most unusual for me, an operator, to meet a prospective client under such conditions, but the Chief was using me as a trump card.

It was plain to see that the president of the power company was in a bad humor. He kept talking about the implicit confidence he had in his employees, and at first he absolutely refused to believe my statement of what I had

[221]

seen. Twice he started to telephone one of his assistants in Fayette, and each time the Chief, obviously remembering his experience in the Centerville power strike, said he would wash his hands of the whole matter if this was done. He was sure someone at the other end would "spill the beans" and if the story of the organizing got out and led to the dismissal of several men it would surely bring on a strike. The attorney was more reasonable, and he seemed to believe what the Chief and I told them.

"You gentlemen seem convinced that I'm a crook and a grafter and I will admit that I have nothing with me at the moment to prove that I'm not," the Chief finally said in his most impressive manner. "I am going to make you a proposition, and you can take it or leave it. But you'll have to accept or reject it definitely tonight. I am going to propose ways and means of settling your labor difficulty in a perfectly legal manner without using any operators at all. The plan I have to propose will not only avert a strike but it will keep your people out of the union. Before I tell you this plan, you will have to sign an agreement we can draw up right here. This agreement will provide that *if* you use the plan I am going to propose and *if* it succeeds, you will pay me five thousand dollars within thirty days after the plan goes into effect, and five thousand dollars more one year from that date. The agreement will provide that the second five thousand dollars will not be paid if you have had a strike during the year."

The president howled to high heaven; but by this time

his attorney had become convinced that the Chief knew
what he was talking about—at least insofar as the actual
existence of agitation among the employees was concerned.
He finally got the president to see that he would not be out
a single penny or be obligated in any way unless he made
use of the plan the Chief was going to suggest.

Suddenly the president calmed down, and I was sent to
my room for my typewriter, and we drew up an agreement. The Chief was evidently an expert in the prepara-
tion of contracts. The attorney argued about nearly every
point and it was easy to see he was looking for some sort
of loophole, but he finally gave in and it was signed by the
Chief, the president of the company, and the attorney.

The Chief then explained the operation of the well-known
"yellow dog contract." He advised the president to go back
to Fayette and have a quantity of these contracts printed
and submit them to employees of all departments immediately and ask to have them signed. The Chief believed
that this would stop Hinds's activities immediately for he
was certain there would be no particular objection to signing
on the part of the big majority of the employees, as in this
instance—unlike the one in Centerville—Hinds had not had
much time to work on the employees. The Chief also strongly recommended that a small wage increase accompany this
proposal.

The president now started to complain about the agreement he had signed and said that he would have thought
of this idea himself if he had taken a little time. The Chief

gave him a lot of advice about how to prepare the employee's non-union agreements and the attorney made copious notes.

"There goes as tight-fisted an employer as I ever saw in my life," remarked the Chief after they had left. "If he refuses to follow my suggestions, he's going to have a strike on his hands just as sure as anything in the world and I'm not going to help him out of it either. He couldn't pay me enough to send my people into his town on a strike job. That guy's spent over a hundred thousand dollars on a lot of phoney antiques but he howls to high heaven because I'm charging him ten thousand to insure industrial peace as long as he lives."

A week later all the employees of the Fayette Light & Power Company were handed a "yellow dog contract" when they received their pay; none—or almost none of them—realized its ominous intent, and they signed at once without even a careful reading. Five of Hinds's recruits, a few die-hards and apostles of "rugged individualism" resigned rather than sacrifice their rights, but nobody seemed to care.

My share of the spoils consisted of five hundred dollars from the first installment of our fee, and a year later the Chief sent me a similar amount. Our client lived up to the terms of his contract, but the Chief said it had been necessary to use quite a little pressure to make him do so.

"As long as things are quiet around your home town," the Chief remarked after the Fayette organizing effort had been averted, "I believe the best thing for you to do is to make an occasional trip like the one you made to Fayette.

There are a dozen cities within two hundred miles of Centerville where we have no clients, and there must be union
activity of some sort in all of them. Arrange to take a
couple of days off every week and start visiting these towns.
You can always frame up some excuse, and with your ability
to get acquainted and learn what is going on, I wouldn't
be surprised if you got a job as good as this last one every
place you went."

I followed the Chief's orders and a good volume of business resulted. But, somehow I kept thinking about Mike
and his wife and their hundreds of friends in Fayette. I'll
never forget Mike's comment on the "yellow dog agreement." His remarks reminded me of the story told of Abra-
ham Lincoln when, as a youth, Lincoln saw the slave market
in New Orleans. He announced that sooner or later he was
going to take a hard crack at the institution of slavery,
and history reveals just how successful he was.

"The yellow dog agreement," said Mike, "is one of the
worst things in America today. A man who is forced to
sign it should realize that his liberty of thought and action,
which is guaranteed by the Constitution, has been taken
away and that there's nothing he can do about it. Sooner
or later, some of us are going to eliminate this thing, and I
don't expect to be too old to have a hand in it when that
time comes."

Mike had to wait only about ten years to make his boast
come true.

[225]

CHAPTER 34

Hard Luck for McGoorty

LABOR meeting after labor meeting. Convention after convention. Deals with various factions. Deals with individuals. But the same general theme prevailed, and variety became increasingly scarce. Several routine, busy years, for the most part happy ones, slipped rapidly by.

Within two years of the inauguration of our partnership McGoorty and I had a bunch of building mechanics as good as any in the United States. Centerville contractors were actually able to revise unit labor costs downward. Out-of-town contractors who had jobs in our city loudly acclaimed the labor conditions they found, and advertised the situation far and wide.

The time was ripe for the shake-down of the contractors that McGoorty and I had planned. He and I talked it over and decided that Mac should be a committee of one to call on them and discuss "the erection of a statue in our honor,

[226]

or something." Mac talked to them and it was agreed that a statue would not do sufficient honor to citizens such as ourselves, who had displayed such outstanding civic interest. Accordingly, Mac agreed to accept "something" to the tune of $1,500 per month from the contractors for an indefinite period. But darned if McGoorty didn't play into the hardest kind of luck. The first payment was to be made in the back room of an undertaking parlor, for want of a better place. Before passing the money the contractors' representative felt called upon to repeat the terms of the arrangement once more, and Mac readily and audibly agreed to them. The money was passed. Mac pocketed it and walked out the back door right into the arms of six policemen. The bills had been marked and a dictaphone had recorded the conversation.

The grand jury returned an indictment on six counts. The case was tried at once, and when it was over Mac had nothing on which to congratulate himself except that his ten-year sentence would be shortened to a little over six if he got a "good conduct" rating while in the penitentiary. As there was no one else to carry on in his place, I picked up the reins of the Building Trades Council, shouted "Giddap," and drove on.

I was soon able to get control of all union organizing activity in the city. Because of my new position as president of the Building Trades Council I was elected vice president of the Central Labor Union. From that time on my work consisted almost entirely of undermining organizing drives, and refusing to condone strikes. The latter was possible as a result of my getting all the local unions in the city to agree not to call a strike unless the entire labor movement would stand solidly behind it. This could come about only with the backing of the Central Labor Union. As long as I was a member of the executive committee of the CLU its approval of a strike of any sort was a remote possibility.

CHAPTER 35

Unions, Horizontal and Vertical

DURING a quiet period in my Centerville affairs, I received a letter from the Chief asking me to come to his office, prepared to be away from home for a week. It developed that he wished me to do some "hooking" in the coal fields. I had heard of the procedure, but never had any experience with it. He gave me a brief general outline to follow and ended up with, "You need only two things to become a good roper. A gift of gab and unlimited gall. The boys we've been sending to do this job didn't have enough of either one, and I'm counting on you."

The Chief also explained the general situation in the coal mines. For a number of years the coal operators and the coal miners' union had worked together under an agreement that was unusually favorable to the union. This agreement called for a one hundred per cent closed shop, meaning that everyone employed in the coal fields must belong to the union. It also stated that each man's dues were to be deducted from his pay by the company paymaster and turned over to the union treasurer on pay-day. This was known as the "checkoff" and the operators' desire to discontinue it was the principal stumbling block in the path of a new agreement.

Both sides refused to yield, and a strike was expected. The coal operators had given the Chief a large order for men to work in the mines. I believe they were principally concerned in getting advance notice of sabotage and determining which workmen, if any, were opposed to a strike and would like to stay on the job. Where we could not get our own men employed in the mines roping men already employed there was the only alternative.

We hear a great deal nowadays about "vertical" and "horizontal" unions. At that time the United Mine Workers of America was the largest and strongest of the vertical organizations. For years it claimed four hundred thousand members. The vertical principle as applied to the coal industry meant that every man who worked inside a coal mine, or around the mouth of the mine, or in any of the buildings or shops or other places of employment in the vicinity of the mine, and connected with it, was eligible for membership in the miners' union. Under the agreement that had been in effect for a number of years it was obligatory for these employees to join the miners' union or they could not work in the territory the agreement covered.

Now compare this with a railroad shop in one of the

large terminal cities where locomotives and cars are repaired and serviced. An engine is driven into the yard by an engineer who is a member of the Brotherhood of Locomotive Engineers. The man who fires the boiler of the engine is a member of the Brotherhood of Locomotive Firemen. The train crew are members of still another union; the men who keep the tracks level and in repair belong to another; and the men in the shops who work on the cars and engines belong to still other unions. All railroad electrical work is done by members of a special union, while the messages sent over railway telegraph lines are dispatched by union telegraphers. The railroad conductor belongs to one union, but his companion who works for the Pullman Company belongs to another. The Pullman porters have a union, and the men who sort the mail in the mail cars have their own organization. If a railroad has agreements with all of these unions, and most of them do, it is necessary to have a large department that does nothing but keep track of these contracts.

This is the "horizontal" idea of trade unionism. I suppose the term originated when it was observed that the different trades and crafts employed by a company could be likened to horizontal layers or strata. Every member of each horizontal layer belonged to a different craft, and therefore was required to join a different union. The guilds that existed in Europe for hundreds of years were organized along similar lines.

It is my opinion that there would be many advantages,

from a union point of view, if every industry were organized along "vertical," "industrial," or CIO lines. (The crafts are still distinct, each receiving wages commensurate with the ability required and the danger involved.) If the employer balks at any clause of a vertical agreement the entire plant can be tied up instantly.

Take a similar situation in an industry with the horizontal plan, the railroads for instance. We will assume that all unions have made satisfactory agreements except the machinists. These men work in the roundhouses and other shops, making repairs on rolling stock. An agreement cannot be reached; so the machinists go on strike. The business of the railroad goes blithely on without serious interruption. The other craftsmen, who are working under satisfactory agreements, pay little or no attention to the complaint of the machinists. Such a strike has a slim chance of being successful.

While discussing the coal situation with the Chief, I asked him why there were so few vertical unions. His reply sounded logical, but no union man on the AFL side will admit it—publicly at least.

"Supposing you are the president of the machinists' union, The International Association of Machinists," said the Chief. "I'm mentioning this union by name; but everything I say applies to any of the larger craft unions. You have a fine fat salary of about twenty-five thousand a year with an expense allowance and a big office in Washington for your headquarters. You have a number of vice presidents and organizers on your staff, and they do most of the leg work while you sit there in your office and draw your pay and look wise. You got your start as a machinist and joined the union and worked your way up to the top of the heap, and now you have one of the best jobs in the world.

"You have several hundred local unions scattered over this country and Canada, with the members in every variety of shop and factory where machinists are employed. Union agreements are in existence in some of these places and you have hopes of getting more agreements and more closed shops all the time. Every once in a while, one of your locals loses a strike and goes out of business, or gets such a wallop it takes years to recover. Suppose you lost a strike in a ship-yard where you had about fifty machinists. In the same shop there were gangs of union carpenters, blacksmiths, boiler-makers, iron workers, firemen and engineers and probably a few other trades. The other union men were sorry for you and your machinists, but as they were satisfied with their own agreement they kept right on working and you lost the strike. Of course there have been instances where all the unions in a shop got together and pulled a united strike, but this happens very rarely.

"Whenever you lose a strike like that, you think, 'Wouldn't it be fine if all the men in that shop belonged to the same union so they would all go on strike at the same time and we would win without any trouble.' You, as president of the machinists' union, probably have that thought every day of your life. But why don't you do something about it?

[233]

You know the presidents of all the other big unions. You are a delegate to the conventions of the American Federation of Labor. You could get up in a convention any time and say, 'Fellows, this is all wrong, we aren't getting anywhere. Let's form one union for the railroad employees, another for the shipyards, another for the building industry and so on.'

"But you don't say that," said the Chief with emphasis, "and I'll tell you why. You don't say it, and you even try to keep from thinking about it for this reason. What would happen to your nice twenty-five-thousand-dollar-a-year job if the unions consolidated along industrial lines? The presidents of the other big unions don't speak about it either. They have their fine fat jobs to hang on to, just as you have. If the metal trades unions such as the machinists, molders, sheet metal workers, iron workers, and all the rest of the dozen or so unions which handle metal were to consolidate, there would be only one president—and that might not be you. If all the carpenters, bricklayers, hod carriers, plumbers, cement finishers, and the other unions which make up the building trades were to get together in one union there would be just one president and that's all. If such a thing took place there would very likely be a flock of vice presidents who would have charge of the various crafts within the vertical union, but that would mean that every one of the presidents of the building trade unions, with only one exception, would have to accept a reduction in rank, and human beings aren't made that way.

"Your union leaders are not different from business men. There would be even more businesses consolidated today than there are, except that too many people with good jobs would be in danger of losing out. I'm as bad as the rest. A few years ago the president of another agency met me several times, and we talked about combining our companies. He had the larger outfit, with more money, and would have been the president. I would have been general manager but I wanted the president's title—so the deal fell through."

CHAPTER 36

By Hook or Crook

THE next day I was driving through the coal country. As a "cover," or excuse for being there, I had secured a dilapidated sedan and filled the rear compartment with books, which I was trying to sell.

In comparison with the modern industrial cities where I had previously lived a mining town is the worst spot on earth. Even the best of them are pretty bad. Dirty children fight and squall in the unpaved streets. Sad-eyed women idle away the daylight hours by gossipping on their porches and screaming at their offspring. With twilight, a Stygian horde debouches from a hundred shafts. The community dines, drinks, fights, prays, sleeps, and at daybreak, every able-bodied male is at the mouth of the pit again. As I saw the miners on this trip, and many times later, I thought they had less to live for than any group of people I had ever encountered.

Our clients had given us the names and addresses of several men in each town who might be good prospects for our work. These men were supposedly the most intelligent and loyal. During the day I would drive around with my load of books, try to sell them to the wives of my prospects, and thus get an idea as to the home life of the men I was stalking. Eventually I would decide to approach one or other of the men on my list, and arrange to meet him after work in the evening. We would go for a ride in the country in my car, and I would present my proposition.

I hired Tom Perona on my first trip. He was a fine young man who stayed with us several years and became a splendid operator and a natural leader. Tom was a bachelor who lived with his mother and six younger brothers and sisters. He was the only regular wage earner in the family and this fact had attracted me to him in the first place. I was certain he could use some extra cash and wouldn't pass up a chance to earn it.

"Tom, I'm in a tough spot. You can help me out and make a little money for yourself if you want to," I said in my most engaging manner when we came to a quiet place and I stopped the car. "I've got the most peculiar job in the world and I'll tell you what it is. You probably know that most of the mines around here are owned by the same company, and that this company has other mines in other parts of the state. There are probably a thousand stockholders, and there are also a lot of bondholders, and these people are the real owners of the property. I work for the company that sold the bonds. We sell bonds for a lot of different companies every year. Our customers buy bonds issued by one company, and if they get their interest regularly for a few years they know the bonds are good, and they'll have confidence in us and come back and buy more bonds the next time we have any for sale. That's just like business in a grocery store. If you like the goods you buy there, you'll come back again.

"Now, it is up to us to keep in touch with the companies whose bonds we sell and see if they're run properly. Of course the officers of these companies let us see their books, but we want more than that. We want to know if the men are treated right, and if the mines are operated safely, and if wages are as good as they are any place else in the community. The people who buy these bonds want their money used properly, and don't want employees to be underpaid or mistreated or be compelled to work under unsafe conditions.

"Now here's where I come in. My job is to go around and talk to the employees of the different companies for which we have sold bonds. I've been at it over five years now and it's the best job I ever had. I haven't had much experience up here in the coal country. Most of my work has been out in Ohio and Indiana and Michigan among the manufacturing plants. What I wanted to see you about was whether you would like a job helping me. I've looked up your record and it seems you're a hard worker, and it's certainly fine of you to be taking care of your family the way you do. If you think you can do this I don't know of a man I'd rather hire because I know you can use the money.

"Here's all you would have to do: I make headquarters over here in Meadsburgh, and I want you to write me a letter every day telling me what is going on in the mine. The main thing I'm interested in is whether the men are satisfied with their work; and whether they are treated right by the foreman, or if he has a lot of his relatives in the best jobs and makes the other fellows do all the heavy work; and if the safety regulations are being carried out."

And I would go on for a long time. If Tom didn't decide I was a boon to the long-suffering coal miner by the time I was through it was only because he was too dumb to understand English. I usually offered such prospects as Tom ten dollars a week if they would write a report every day. The usual rate for an operator was two dollars a day and up. A lot of the good ones got three dollars. The Chief charged the same rate for the men we roped as the others, but we made twenty-five to fifty dollars a month more on them.

"Tom, you never saw me until today," I concluded; "you don't know whether I'm a crook, or the most honest guy in the world. On the other hand I know a good deal about you. I've seen your home and talked to your mother and found out a good deal about your record at the mine. I hear you're just about the best checkweighman they ever had. This means I can trust you and I'm willing to do it. But all you know about me is what I've told you.

[239]

"Now here's what I'll do if you want to make a start at this. I'll just stake you to a five spot to show my good faith. This will be pay in advance for about three letters. You write me one tomorrow. I'll reply right away, telling you I got it, and giving you advice about how to write the next one. In fact, I'll be writing you just about as often as you write me. Any time you don't think I'm treating you right you can quit and we'll still be good friends. How about it?"

Tom agreed and I hired him. Most men fell for the idea, and the single ones went through with it nearly every time. A married man usually wanted to talk it over with his wife and she, good soul, could be counted on to scare him out more often than not. It finally got so I wouldn't make a cash advance to a married man. Time after time we waited for days to hear from a married man. Then a letter would arrive saying he and the wife had talked it over and decided to pass it up.

If a man wasn't "roped," or "hooked," at the first interview, it wasn't considered wise to see him again. He might show up with a gang who had ideas of their own about roping. If an operator talked to three or four men in the same community without being able to hire any of them, it was no longer safe for him to operate there, and another man would have to come in and make the approach along different lines. This was the reason for my trip to the mines. Most of our office men had tried and failed.

I never ran out of stories to tell the men I employed. I

might say I was a newspaper reporter assigned to cover the entire coal field. I wanted news of all phases of the mining industry and my company, a mythical news syndicate, had given me permission to employ a man in each section to act as a reporter and keep me informed. No, he mustn't announce his connection with us. It wouldn't be safe. Miners might think he was using his position to work against them. It would be much better if he said nothing about it to anyone, even his own family. Or possibly I was in the employ of a mining equipment company that furnished all kinds of machinery and safety devices for mines. I wanted to meet the best miner in each mine and get his suggestions for the improvement of mining machinery. We wanted to make the finest product in the world and were coming right to the miner himself to ask his advice. I also hooked several men by telling them I was a writer on economic subjects, and was making a study of the miner and his economic condition.

And how did we manage to make these fellows obey instructions when it came to handling union meetings and reporting on union activity? No effort at all was made to do this for a couple of weeks. By this time, the man was better acquainted with us. He had received a nice friendly letter every few days that not only advised him regarding his reports but chatted about current events, the political situation, told him a funny story now and then and displayed a great personal interest in him and his affairs. If there was a baby in the family, a little present was sure to find its way to his home. If he was courting a girl, notice was taken of this and some appropriate recognition was made. And he got paid right on time.

We had lived up to our promises, possibly given him a slight increase in pay. Would he be inclined to get up on his high horse simply because we wanted to know the details of a union meeting? Should he fluke simply because we advised him to preach caution to his fellows if they decided to burn a trestle when the strike started?

And when the strike finally came, his only income was from us.

When I had finally made my deal with Tom, or any of the others, I gave explicit instructions about where to send the reports, always a post-office box in a city where we had an office. Tom had no post-office box himself so I told him to get one. This would prevent his mail from falling into unfriendly hands. I went under the name of Martin Ott. I told him to address me by my initials, MO, and to use this salutation in his correspondence. To keep his name out of my letters to him, I would cudgel my brains (for his benefit) and dig up a "code" like KV-133 and tell him to sign this to his letters and I would address him in that fashion when I wrote.

With hearty manifestations of good will I would then say farewell and go on to the next town, in quest of more hookees. In the meantime, I would advise the office to be on the lookout for Tom's reports and relate the details of his employment. The office men would reply to Tom's letters when they arrived, sign them with my code, MO, and the hookee would never know the difference.

Eventually it would become necessary for the office men to meet these operators. A letter would be sent them by "MO," announcing his departure for distant fields and the transfer of his business to BOS or one of the other superintendents in the office. BOS, himself a past master at getting under the skin of an operator, would then go to visit Tom, and in most cases get along famously, and the operation would continue.

Many of these roped coal miners did wonderful work, from our point of view. When a strike was called we knew almost to a man who was loyal and who would walk out. We also knew which men were the trouble makers, and which would counsel caution. I was out of the coal picture by this time and back at my other work, but the boys in our coal district offices kept me informed of the outstanding achievements of the men I had employed. This was how I came to know Tom Perona better.

One night at a union meeting after the strike had started he saw that violence was unavoidable. The men had been out for about six weeks and were starting to feel the first pinch of hunger and defeat. A desperate mood was on many of them. They decided to fire the tipple at two o'clock the following morning. Only eight men were in on the deal and Tom was one of them. Midnight arrived.

After exhausting every means of dissuading them, he slipped away and ran the entire eight miles to the next town and got there at one o'clock. I know those mountain roads after dark and I wouldn't have believed it of any man in the world except Tom Perona. He phoned the mine superintendent and gave him warning. The state troopers arrived at the mine just in time to avert a loss of thousands of dollars and arrest three of the culprits who were pouring oil on the structure. Tom was at once suspected and was lucky to escape with his life. When I learned of it, I had him come to Centerville where a job was found for him, and soon we put him to work operating in the regular way. His mother and the younger children joined him and they were the happiest people in the world to be away from the coal country. Tom told me several years later that he was pretty sure when I hired him that the information he turned in was for the benefit of the mine owners.

CHAPTER 37

Hooking in the Dark

As a result of the success we had in the coal fields with hooked men, the same plan was followed in shops and factories on those rare occasions when it was impossible to get our people employed in the regular manner. I recall an experience in a neighboring town that was largely given over to industrial plants, many of which were owned by corporations with headquarters located in other places. Our contacts would be with the president, or perhaps the general manager; but when we sent our men to the plants themselves they were refused employment as long as there were local people out of work. It therefore became necessary to hook a few men, and I was asked to undertake the job.

With no advance information regarding the city, its layout, or its inhabitants, I examined a city map, located the plants I wanted, and started out to find them. They were fine modern structures employing several thousand people. I found hundreds of workmen's houses in the vicinity. It would not be hard to find men employed in our client's shops, but I had been instructed to hook a toolmaker in one, and a metal finisher in another. How to proceed was a problem.

Leaving my car at noon, I walked along several streets lined with small houses in which workmen undoubtedly lived. I chatted with several children on their way home from school. Did their father work in the Motor Company? No, he worked in the foundry, but the man who lived in the green house worked in the Motor plant. Yes, he'd worked there a long time and his name was Johnson. I made a note of the number and name. Several other names and addresses were picked up in this manner from storekeepers and deliverymen, and by mid-afternoon I started calling on them. In nearly every instance I found a wife or a mother at home. I couldn't help comparing these clean and charming houses with the filth and squalor I had seen in the mining district.

"Madam," I said at the first home I visited, "I am looking for a family named Johnson who formerly lived in Chicago and came here some twenty years ago. I'm not sure of the first name but it was either Alfred or Albert (This was the way the kids had given it to me). I am an attorney and we are trying to find these people to settle an estate."

There is no more certain way to arouse the curiosity of the average person than to let him suspect he has a chance of getting something for nothing. The Mrs. Johnson to whom I talked hadn't come from Chicago, and she knew of no one who had, but she was willing to tell me about all the Johnsons in her family, as well as every other Johnson in the city. I would casually inquire about her husband and his occupation. Yes, he was employed at the Motor Company as a machinist. No, he wasn't a toolmaker, although he had often thought of learning the trade, which was not greatly different from that of a machinist, but paid better. I'd heard a vague rumor to the effect that the Johnson I was seeking was a toolmaker. Well, now, wasn't that odd? Mrs. Johnson would remark. There was a man named Johnson who had been a toolmaker in the lamp factory, but he no longer worked there. And so on.

Sooner or later I would run across someone who knew the toolmakers in the Motor Company plant; I would learn a few names; and finally I would interview one or more of them, and hook my man. The same procedure worked out in my quest for a metal finisher. Once a man in the proper department was located, the story would be about the same as at the mines.

I have nothing but pleasant memories of this town. The toolmaker I finally located was a splendid, ambitious man of about thirty-five, with a wife and two of the prettiest little girls I ever saw. He refused to leave his home to talk to me, and I could readily see he was suspicious. No, if I had anything to say, I could say it right there in his living room in front of his wife. I'd never done such a thing, but I was getting desperate; I'd been there five days, and seemingly was no closer to landing a toolmaker than when I started. (The metal finisher had been easy.) I took a chance on it, making my principal play in the direction of the woman. I never tried to sway a labor or political audience any harder than I did the toolmaker and his wife that night. In the end I got him.

This chap was with us for a number of years. His wife had been a stenographer before they married. She typed while he dictated, and the reports were models, not only of typing, but of composition and subject matter. He had a most analytical mind, coupled with outstanding mechanical ability. When we no longer had any need of him in this particular job I got word to him about an opportunity in another city, which eventually resulted in his becoming assistant superintendent of a large plant.

Hooking was also a favorite means of employing operators in public utilities and on the railroads. These industries have seniority rules, and although it was not hard to get a man employed, it might be years before he secured a position where anything of importance could be learned.

Over a period of several years I made a good many contacts with employees in these industries. The procedure was always about the same. I would start them writing to us on some pretext. Soon they were following instructions to the letter. I'm absolutely sure that in the large majority of these cases, the men knew pretty well what was wanted before I had finished talking. Those who didn't usually got onto it in short order. Yet I can't remember a single instance where a hooked man got wise, and fluked because he had been misled.

And this is all there is to the hooking, or roping phase of the labor spy business. Men who claim to have been hooked, and then led on for years without ever discovering just what they had got themselves into, are in my opinion, either utter fools, or liars.

CHAPTER 38

Sludge Gang

NEXT to the "yellow dog" contract, company unions were the worst thorn in the side of labor leaders during the twenties. The "yellow dog" was finally legislated out of existence, while the effectiveness of the company union was dealt three damaging blows by the NRA, then the CIO, and finally the Wagner Law.

My interest in company unions started shortly after the coal hooking episode. About fifty miles from Centerville was an oil refinery. It was the terminus of a pipe line that brought crude oil from the fields of Texas or Oklahoma. From a small beginning this refinery had grown to enormous size, and employed about two thousand men. To take care of further expansion, the company was arranging to float a large bond issue. There was a good demand for such securities at that time, but even so it was considered essential to avoid labor troubles while the new financing was going on. The Chief was called in for advice and he suggested a plan that was approved. This conference took place some ten months before the securities were to be placed on the market and he had plenty of time to put his program into effect.

I was sent to the city in question, and for several days I hunted for a union man of any description. I finally found one; the railway telegrapher. Outside of this isolated individual there was no union material on which organizers could build. One of our Communist operators also looked high and low for any sign of Communism and found none.

The Chief suggested that all the employees of the company be "allowed" to form an association that would have some small part in the management of the company's affairs. Each department would elect one or two delegates to a "plant committee." Once a month the plant manager would meet with this group for a discussion of any business that might properly come before it.

It was expected that the subjects for committee discussion would be safety, sanitation and sports, as well as suggestions for the improvement of production and economical operation. In short, the committee was to have all the opportunity it desired to talk about everything except raising wages and decreasing hours of work. These subjects were taboo, but it might be mentioned in passing that these two subjects are the principal ones with which a labor union, once it has been "recognized," is concerned. The company had several plants in addition to the refinery, and each plant

[251]

would have a committee of this sort. Each plant committee was to elect delegates to the "General Committee," which would meet with the president and general manager twice a year and talk things over.

Every member of the company union would be made to take out an insurance policy. They were to be allowed to use the company gymnasium, and would receive tickets to all the dances and the annual picnic. These privileges were to be in return for payment of nominal dues. The association would also publish a monthly "house organ" and give prizes for the best articles and photographs.

There were thousands of such associations in those days. Nearly every large company had something of the sort. The idea was, of course, if a union organizer came around, he would be told, "Oh, we have our own union already, and we talk things over with the company officials whenever we want to."

To make the thing doubly safe, the Chief sold the client on the idea of placing an operator in each department, who would do his level best to secure election to the plant committee. If we could get a few of our own men elected it was a pretty safe bet that they would be able to keep the other members within safe and sane limits. Our operators could also exert a restraining influence on the men in their departments if this was necessary, and thus provide further protection against labor unrest. The bill would be high, but nothing compared with the loss that would result from a strike at the time the new bonds were being issued.

The refinery had eleven departments, which meant that eleven shop operators would be employed. It was possible to send experienced men for eight of the jobs, but the three others were in departments where there was seldom any change of personnel; so I was sent over to hook the people we needed. Our client gave us the names of men he thought might be approachable, and this was a great help.

The chap I hooked in the shipping department was a personable young bachelor, and lived with his sister and her husband, who was a rural mail carrier. This youngster's only fault was shyness. "Here's the worst thing that can happen to you," I told him. "Suppose you step up to a man and start talking to him. He can hit you over the head, and then throw you out into the street. Don't let that worry you. You won't feel the second bump at all. Anyway, the chances are a hundred to one that you'll make a friend."

The company team was just starting baseball practice when I got acquainted with MC-311, as we called him on the books. Of course, he made the team, and this gave him a certain prestige, as the town was baseball crazy. The team played at least one game each week with clubs representing other plants in near-by towns. I suggested to 311 that he develop a definite diamond personality, and after I discovered that he had a regular fog-horn voice (when he could be induced to let it loose) I soon had him giving a fine imitation of Joey Sewell—to the delight of the fans and the appreciation of his teammates.

His shyness overcome, 311 was soon on his way to becom-

[253]

ing a leader in the shipping department. He was elected one of the two delegates to the shop committee. The other delegate was an elderly fellow whom everyone liked, but who was not particularly aggressive. 311 was able to reason with him and get his support in every matter of importance. This fixed the shipping department nicely.

The second man I hooked was in the office. He was a bachelor also, and almost the only one in the department. Most of the office help were women, and for a while I had thought of hooking one of them and trying to get her elected as a delegate. Finally, however, I decided on a man, for a somewhat unusual reason. The fellow I picked was a nice-looking, rather feminine young chap. Such men are generally popular with women. He was elected, and served satisfactorily on the committee for several years.

As for the third: I don't recall the name of the department, but the men employed in it spent most of their time wading around in the sludge left in the tanks after the oil is drained off. Their job was to get the tanks cleaned out and ready for the next filling. Three of our best operators had taken a crack at this job, but the longest any of them could last was a week. (This was several days longer than I would have stayed.)

So I was asked to hook one of the regular crew, and a strange lot they were. The foreman was a Croat and most of the regular members of the gang were from Montenegro. None of them spoke any English, nor any language I knew. One of them, however, had been a fisherman in his youth, and had sailed the Adriatic long enough to pick up a few words of the most barbarous Italian dialect that I had ever heard. We could understand each other after a fashion, but he could neither read nor write. In desperation, I hired him. Once a week I made a trip to see him, and he gave me a verbal report (with gestures) on his department in exchange for a five-dollar bill. To this day I do not know how his name was spelled or pronounced, but on our books he was MC-317. We became fast friends. I still think of him as the most unconventional operator I have ever known.

The entire gang hated the foreman, according to him, partly because of his nationality, and partly because of his dictatorial manner. When I told 317 that if the management knew exactly what type of man the foreman was he would surely be fired, he protested violently, and said that they had had three other foremen during the past six years, and this one was so much superior to the others that none of the men would think of a change. They would be sure to get a foreman who was infinitely worse.

I'd informed 317 that I expected him to become the delegate from his department to the shop committees. He promised to try, but he didn't seem very hopeful. The balloting in these shop elections was informal; that is, there were no nominations from the floor. The three names receiving the largest number of ballots were voted on again. If one received a majority, he was elected. Otherwise the name with the lowest number of votes was dropped out, and the two high ones fought it out.

[255]

The election in his department must have been a circus. As far as I could find out from him, each man voted for himself. This went on for several ballots. Someone then suggested that slips of paper be placed in a hat, one for each man in the department. These would then be drawn by the men in turn, and the two who got slips with pencil crosses on them would be the delegates. My man was one of those charged with preparing the slips, and he palmed one of the marked ones.

He would steal anything he could lift, and he was a giant. One time he told me about a theft of a lot of lumber by one of his co-workers. He then went on to revile the thief for having taken the lumber, when he, 317, had already decided to take it himself. His salary at the plant did not quite permit him to live in the style he desired. As he had no other source of income, he decided it was up to the plant to provide it. He explained that he carried off enough company property to make up the difference.

Of the twelve or so workers in the sludge gang eight or nine were Montenegrins, and the remainder were floaters who drifted in for a short time, and then moved on because they could not endure the work. At least, this was what I assumed from the reports of our operators who tried it out for a few days and then quit. But according to 317 when the gang reported for work in the morning the old-timers and the foreman retired to some secluded spot, possibly the bottom of a tank, where they lapsed into peaceful slumber until noon or thereabouts. The drifters, under the supervision of

one of the regular crew, were set to work on the hardest
job to be found, and made to toil unceasingly throughout
the day, or until they threw up the sponge and quit. During
the afternoon, the regulars did a certain amount of work
themselves.

"Don't they ever catch you asleep?" I asked 317 in amaze-
ment.

No, this had never happened. One man was always on
watch and he gave warning of the approach of the superintendent, or other officials. After a couple of hours the man
assigned to watch would waken one of the others who would
relieve him, and so it went. The foreman was never called
to account for not getting more work done. No one in
authority seemed to have a very good idea as to what should
be expected from such a crew, and they lived a life of bliss-
ful ease. For reasons I don't understand very well myself,
I revolted against reporting the escapades of this likable
opéra-bouffe troupe—but I finally did.

CHAPTER 39

Clean Sweep

THE plant was a nest of thieves. Thousands of dollars' worth of equipment was going out every week in the pockets and automobiles of the employees. The thievery was first discovered by one of our old operators who was working as a millwright. He saw men in his department openly putting company property into their automobiles. The equipment he saw being stolen included all sorts of tools, pipe fittings, brass pieces, rubber boots and clothing, oil, soap, cloth by the bolt, office supplies, lumber, and all sorts of building material.

The police had orders to search each car leaving the grounds, and make every employee open any packages he might have. The police were actually doing neither, although they generally went through the motions of looking into the cars. Our millwright got a lift to his home one night in the car of one of his fellow workers. He had seen the man place ten new two-inch brass globe valves on the floor in the rear of his car that afternoon, and throw an old coat over them. That evening when he passed the police officer at the main gate, the officer looked into the rear compartment through the window, and waved his hand as a signal to drive on. Had he moved the coat, he would have seen some fifteen or twenty dollars' worth of new valves.

My baseball player, MC-311, gave us the hottest piece of news. The refinery used an enormous amount of pipe of all sizes. They were always running lines in all directions for one purpose or another, and then taking them up. If it was bent, or damaged in any way, it was sold for scrap. When a carload had accumulated it was shipped away to the scrap dealer who had bid successfully for it. At the same time, they bought a great deal of pipe of the grade known as "seconds." This was used by the millwrights for making railings, and in other kinds of construction work where it was not necessary for the pipe to stand any internal pressure.

311 had a phenomenal memory for railway car numbers. This was almost a necessity for anyone working in the shipping department, as nearly all the shipments of oil and gasoline were in tank cars. He had shipped a gondola of scrap the winter before I became acquainted with him, and a couple of weeks later had seen the same car in the company yards. He wondered at this, and climbed up on the side. The car was filled with pipe, and he decided after some reflection

[259]

that it must have been delayed, and not pulled out by the rail-road. Such a thing was possible as there were a couple of miles of track in the refinery grounds.

On looking it up in his records, however, he found that the car had been signed for in the usual manner by the rail-road, and further search showed that it had been delivered to the proper consignee in a town two hundred miles away. Next he discovered that the very same car of pipe he had shipped two weeks before had been delivered to the plant on a regular purchase order. It had been sold as "pipe scrap," but had been bought back as "pipe seconds," and had been accepted by the inspectors for use by the millwrights and construction departments. The net loss to the company was about four hundred dollars.

"No wonder this outfit needs to float a bunch of bonds to keep in business," the Chief said. "Think of it. Here's a company worth millions, with a nation-wide business, and its stock listed on the big board. There are a lot of brainy men at the head of it, and from what I've seen of their operations they're just about the best merchandisers in the country. They could sell oil-burning furnaces to the Hottentots, and make them like it, but that's all they can do. I've seen a lot of poorly run plants in my time, but this is the worst. I wish to heaven I'd taken this job on a contingent basis, with a commission on what we could save them. The old president squawked like a stuck pig when I told him what the job was going to cost, but he's going to make a big profit if he's bright enough to straighten out the mess we're uncovering."

This thievery was going on all through the plant, and in a week or so every operator had reported it. When the client read the reports he asked to have a man sent to the town to work on the outside and endeavor to learn what became of all this stuff. There was too much of it for the people to use and the assumption was that it was sold.

The detective the Chief assigned discovered that two or three times a week a junk dealer came to town with a truck and drove about, much as all junk dealers do. He made stops, however, at only a few places—the homes of the principal offenders, where he collected whatever salable plunder they had been able to carry out of the plant. The arrest of this man was carried out just as he was leaving town one day. Since he was unable to give a satisfactory explanation of how he had come by his load, a stop was put to his activity.

As soon as the bond issue had been subscribed, and the immediate danger of labor troubles was past, over one hundred homes were searched by the sheriff and local police simultaneously. The amount of company property discovered was appalling. The thieves were all discharged, and the most flagrant cases were prosecuted. I genuinely regretted the passing of my Montenegrin friend. (The thought of 311 behind prison bars had been more than I could endure, so a few days before the raid I weakened and convinced him that he should dispose of his plunder. He was not among the motley crew corralled by the police, so I assume he followed my advice.)

CHAPTER 40

On the Spot

AFTER disposing of Bradley and McGoorty, I had been able to dominate Centerville organized labor without much competition, but finally trouble developed from a most unexpected source. I was walking along the street one day when a huge sedan stopped at the curb, and Weaver, business agent of the truck drivers' union, called to me. His driver was a giant negro; and there was a white man of similar proportions on the driver's seat with him.

"Hop in and I'll take you over to Yorkville for lunch," said Weaver after we had exchanged greetings. "I've got to see one of my people over there. We'll eat at the Inn and get back here by three o'clock."

This man had come to Centerville about the time I had, and got a job with a trucking contractor. In a few months he bought a truck of his own, and inside of two years he had built up a fleet of six dump trucks, and two or three others.

Suddenly he sold his trucking business, and devoted all his time to the truck drivers' local, of which he was a member. The officers were all elderly men from the horse-and-wagon days, and they offered no opposition to Weaver's activity in building up the union. In a short time, he had one of the largest locals in the city, and he ruled it with an iron hand. Although he attended all meetings of the Central Labor Union, he seldom showed much interest in the proceedings unless they had to do with the trucking business, and then he would come to the fore and announce his stand in a loud, unpleasant voice. He was not popular with the other labor officials, who were inclined to fear and distrust him.

Recently, he had been picked up by the police several times, and questioned in connection with vice raids and bootlegging, but had not been held or actually arrested. He spent much of his time at a roadhouse on the edge of the city, and people who claimed to know said this was the headquarters of his racketeering interests. (He had an office in the Labor Hall where he handled his union affairs.) In his movements about the city he was always accompanied by one or more rough-looking characters, who were popularly supposed to be his bodyguards.

I had been trying to learn more about Weaver for several years. This might be a good opportunity and I readily accepted his invitation. The negro drove so fast that I was on the point of expostulating several times. I noticed that he waved each time we passed a police officer, who would salute in reply, apparently not in the least concerned at the pace we were setting.

[263]

Weaver and I chatted of current events, and then got to talking shop as all labor men eventually do.

"I've got damn' near everything on wheels organized around here," bragged Weaver, "except the kids on roller skates, and I might have them before the summer's over. The last taxi driver was signed up last week and in a few days I'll have all the newspaper drivers. They were a tough bunch, but when I talked turkey to a few of them they decided to come in."

A couple of miles outside of Centerville we passed a two-ton truck loaded with paper scrap. Weaver leaned forward and said something to his driver I couldn't hear. We turned a corner shortly and the driver stopped at the bottom of a small gully. The car was halted in such a position that it blocked the road, and in a few seconds the truck I had noticed came to a stop behind us.

"Here's a guy I want to talk to," said Weaver. "Let's get out and look him over." All four of us got out.

"Climb down off there," Weaver said. I saw that the sign on the side of the truck cab announced membership in some independent truck owners' association. "So you thought I was kidding?" Weaver continued. "Maybe I was, but I'm not any more. Gus [to the man who had sat with our driver], take this guy down the road a piece."

Gus took the truckman by the arm, and pushed him roughly toward the front seat of the automobile. They both got in and Gus drove rapidly away. The look on the truckman's face was one of terror, but he made no objections.

[264]

"Give her the works, Joe," said Weaver to the negro chauffeur.

Mounting the driver's seat, Joe drove the truck to the side of the road. While it was still in motion he stepped out of the cab, and down to the ground. The truck careened along the edge of the bank for a few feet, and then tipped crazily over, landing on its side ten feet below.

Weaver's car returned with Gus in the driver's seat—alone.

Joe, the chauffeur, opened the luggage compartment in the rear of the sedan, and took out two ten-pound sledges, with handles about twelve inches long. Then, as if it were the most routine operation in the world, he climbed down the embankment, opened the hood of the truck on the upper side, and, with a sledge in each hand, proceeded to smash the engine casting to bits.

"It's a shame the way you have to handle some of these punks," Weaver remarked in a perfectly conversational tone of voice as he lit a cigar. "I told this one three times he'd have to join up if he wanted to operate. He must've thought I was just talking for exercise. Now his truck's gone and he can't blame anyone but himself."

Joe put his sledges away and we got into the sedan once more. Still no word about the truckman.

"Let's get on over to Yorkville," said Weaver. "I've got to be back by three no matter what happens."

I rapidly ran over my years of experience in the labor world to find a precedent for an appropriate remark to make under such circumstances, but there seemed to be none. I was a taciturn companion for the rest of the trip. Weaver talked and chatted as usual.

Three days later Weaver phoned me at my house in the evening. He wanted to see me right away. I told him to come over. He was there in ten minutes. I asked him to sit down, but he dispensed with all preliminaries or social graces.

"I'm coming into the Building Trades Council," he said as soon as he entered the room. "Arrange to have the truckmen proposed for membership at the next meeting. I'll let you run things until the end of the year. Then I'm taking over. I'll cut you in for a couple of grand as a bonus for getting out real peaceable."

Weaver's attitude was the height of insolence. Now I could understand the display of power I had been permitted to witness a few days ago. I was supposed to be impressed, and turn over my dearly-won spoils without protest.

"You get nothing," I said with finality. "I'm the boss of the Building Trades, and I'm staying right there, and you stay right where you are—on the outside. My book doesn't say anything about truck drivers being any part of the building business, and as long as I'm running the show, they don't get in."

"Listen, punk," said Weaver a little sadly. "You're a good guy, and I'm trying to be nice about this, but I ain't got time to talk. I'll give you one more chance, and only one. Don't you really think you'd better change your mind?"

"I'm changing nothing except the looks of your map if you

don't get out of here and stay out,"I said, losing my temper, and starting towards him.

He opened the door. Joe, the giant black driver, and Gus, the white man, stood there.

"This guy wants to have his mind changed," said Weaver. The two gangsters came in, and advanced on me from different sides. I recall rushing at one of them with the idea I might be able to knock them out in turn, but somehow it didn't work out that way.

An hour later I regained consciousness. The ticking of the mantel clock was the first thing I noticed. It was eight o'clock. I remembered that it had been seven when Weaver came. I lay on the floor in my living room, and when I tried to get up it was impossible. Slowly and methodically I moved my arms and legs in turn, and decided they weren't broken. There was a terrible pain on one side. Although I didn't know it at the time three of my ribs had been fractured. Finally I was able to crawl to the bedroom and reach the phone. Once more I called the Legion ambulance, and was delighted to get the same prompt service as on the other occasion years before.

CHAPTER 41

Last Laugh

I was discharged from the hospital on the tenth day. Instead of going home, I took a cab to a small hotel near the railroad station. I had managed to get a call through to the Chief a few days before, and told him I was in the hospital having my tonsils removed, an operation he knew I had been considering for a long time.

As for the future I had just two alternatives: I could sneak out of town like a whipped cur, or stay and make a fight. If I fought it must be single-handed, as, for various reasons, there wasn't a soul on whom I cared to call for help. If I ran out I was washed up all over the country, so far as the organized labor movement was concerned.

I suppose the main reason why I didn't say anything about all this to the Chief was pride. I had come to Centerville alone and unknown, and in just a few years had become the leading laborite in the city. My authority had been challenged, and successfully it seemed. I couldn't picture myself going to the Chief and saying, "These big boys beat me up. What'll I do now?" Somehow, the whole thing seemed one for me to handle in my own way, and the less said to anyone the better. The days I lay in bed gave me an excellent opportunity to lay my plans.

For fear Weaver's men might be watching my own car I rented an automobile at one of the newly opened Drive-It-Yourself places, and drove to the armory where my National Guard units were located. I returned to the hotel with two army revolvers, a picket pin, some rope, bandages, and enough ammunition to win a good-sized battle. I rested until midnight, and then drove to the roadhouse where Weaver was known to spend his evenings. His car was parked in the yard, and the negro chauffeur lolled behind the wheel, asleep. The window beside him was open. I walked over to the side of the sleeping driver and awakened him by placing the muzzle of one of my guns against his ear. His eyes opened and rolled in my direction, but he didn't move.

"Get out on this side and walk ahead of me," I said softly. He obeyed, the gun muzzle in the center of his back. I marched him down the road some two hundred yards, and then into a deserted farmyard. I remembered the hard time I'd had knocking Bradley out that night a few years back. Things were different now, and I applied my picket pin to the top of the negro's skull without the slightest hesitation. He crumpled, and in a few minutes I had him trussed and gagged.

[269]

Then I dragged him into a tumbledown old shed. I'd removed his overcoat first, and now I put it and his cap on.

Returning to Weaver's car, I got into the driver's seat and settled down as low as possible, hoping for the best. I waited two hours. Finally Weaver came out. He was alone, slightly intoxicated, and when he flung himself into the back seat he said thickly, "Let's go home."

I drove as rapidly as I had seen the negro drive for a mile, and then brought the car slowly to a stop. I got out and opened the door of the tonneau. Weaver straightened up a little, blinking, and I hit him on the jaw. He slumped to the floor of the car. After tying him tightly, I waited an hour and drove back to the roadhouse. The place was dark. I lifted Weaver from his car to mine, and returned to town without anyone's being the wiser.

Arriving at my apartment house I found the lobby deserted, and I carried Weaver right up to my rooms without detection. When he came to we had a nice quiet talk, and settled a lot of things.

The first thing I had Weaver do was sign a statement to the effect that he had set his thugs on me ten days before. The next thing he did was sign a statement admitting that he had directed the destruction of the truck we had encountered on the highway. I also bluffed him into admitting the destruction of nine other trucks under similar circumstances. He then obliged by confessing he had been in the bootlegging business for several years, and named the politicians who had been protecting him. He also signed a statement describing his connection with the vice wave the city was undergoing.

As to how Weaver came to do all this signing—I had just read a gangster story in one of the popular magazines in which one of the characters was quite ingeniously induced to reveal a lot of information. I gave Weaver every opportunity to think I was going to utilize the same sort of ingenuity. I guess I really would have gone through with it, too; but he wilted, and the elaborate paraphernalia I let him see wasn't needed.

Next I phoned Mike, getting him out of bed at six in the morning. Naturally I'd thought of calling the Chief at this point, and I probably should have. But at that moment I was so unstrung and miserable that I wanted some one who was more of a friend than a business associate.

I simply told Mike I needed his help at once. He didn't stop to ask why. He arrived in less than five hours, although Fayette is almost two hundred miles from Centerville. His wife was with him.

Mike got the story in a moment; but he thought the thing over for almost an hour before suggesting a course of action.

"This thing can be handled in only one way," he announced finally. "For a couple of years I've been hearing about racketeers getting into the labor movement. This is the first time we've had them in this state, and I think we can make an example out of this louse that will scare the others out. You've got these confessions, and I'll sign them as a witness, and the missus can sign them too. The trouble with these things is that they don't always hold in court.

[271]

If we turn this fellow over to the police, they'll let him out on bail, and God knows when we'll be able to get him tried. The thing for us to do is get a prosecuting attorney who'll hit this thing hard and do it quickly.

"The Centerville prosecutor is under fire right now for the way he's been handling the charges of bribery against the county commissioners. I happen to know the governor is pretty sore about this, and he's been thinking about appointing a special prosecutor to handle it. The governor's never stood well in Centerville, and there's no good reason for it. He's a good guy and a square-shooter. I think if he stepped in and took charge it would get him a lot of friends. I'm going to put him wise to this mug, and see if he won't go into action right away. If he does, and gives us a real prosecutor, we can have this fellow before a grand jury in a few hours, get an indictment, and put him over the road in a week. Unless you think I'm all wet, I'll phone the governor right away, and tell him the story."

Of course I agreed. This was the first time I'd ever seen Mike in any role except that of genial host or entertainer. Somehow, though, I'd felt he was no glue-foot when action was required. I don't think any man in the world could have doped out a saner plan, and put it into effect so rapidly.

"Of course," Mike added, as an afterthought, "the fact that you and I started these fireworks isn't going to do us any harm with the governor, or the voters either. That isn't the reason I'm doing it, but it's a fact just the same."

The governor said it sounded all right to him, but he

wanted to have his Centerville manager look the thing over first. My old friend, Irving Gerber, the Centerville manager of the Governor's political party, was at my house in less than half an hour. Gerber phoned the governor in a few minutes, telling him that the whole set-up was a "natural," and was told to proceed with the case, and that the writ of appointing him a special prosecutor would be issued immediately.

Possibly political expediency spurred his efforts, but the record is there for all to read. In exactly twelve days Weaver was indicted, tried, found guilty of five charges, and lodged in the state penitentiary. As far as racketeering jail sentences go this was one of the few instances of where the prison terms were not to run concurrently, but were consecutive. I think the total amounted to fifty-five years. Gerber was the man of the hour, and the governor received the hearty thanks of the community—and carried our county in the next election.

After Weaver had been officially arrested, and every one of his henchmen had been safely put away (also unusual), I spent several quiet days in my apartment with Mike and his splendid wife. Although I had been seemingly strong and well when discharged from the hospital, the intense excitement had brought on a relapse and I was completely exhausted.

"Forget it," Mike said when I tried to express my gratitude. "We're square now, that's all. You came down to Fayette to help me a few years ago when Hinds and I were trying to organize the linemen. It wasn't your fault the company got the jump on us and gave the men the 'yellow dog' before we could get started. I'll be after you again one of these days for something else."

As soon as I was able to get around again I took a week off, and went to visit our home office. The Chief had been on the point of coming to see just what was up, for I hadn't communicated with the office except for the call saying I was in the hospital having my tonsils removed. I told the Chief part of the story, but not all of it. Somehow I couldn't tell the Old Man that I'd taken Weaver's shoes and stockings off and held a lighted candle ready to burn the soles of his feet unless he signed the confessions I put in front of him.

"There are a few things about this I'm telling no one, and that means you, too," I told him when he pressed me for all the details. "You wanted results, and you got them, and that's all I'm saying."

"All right, 99," the Chief said. "I think I understand, and I want you to know that whatever you did suits me, except that I'm afraid you risked your life. I don't want you ever to do that again so long as you work for me. It's not a case of dollars or cents, but because none of these clients are worth it. They wouldn't do the same for you or me. A while back I said you were a real operative, and had done everything but fluke. If what I suspect about this case is true I don't know but what you had a right to walk off the job. I'm mighty glad you didn't, and I'm going to see to it that these clients of ours are given a chance to show their appre-

ciation for what you did for them." The appreciation took
the form of a good-sized remittance a few weeks later.

The convention of the state Federation of Labor met
in August that year as usual. Mike was chairman of the
resolutions committee. He asked me to be present when
he read his report, but I refused, saying I was sick and
tired of hearing a thousand "Whereases." He was firm,
however—one of the few times I'd seen him in that mood;
so of course I promised to be there. The session at which
the resolutions are read generally has a poor attendance as
there is never any debate, and the reading of the long list
of condolences to the families of bereaved members, which
constitute most of the resolutions, is of little interest. That
day, however, most of the delegates were present. After
an hour, my attention was arrested by Mike, reading as
follows:

"WHEREAS, the union labor movement in the
country and this state is dependent on the inspired activity of its members for growth and progress; and

"WHEREAS, a situation recently came into existence in one of the cities of this state, which was un-
precedented in the annals of union history, and which
threatened to disrupt and eventually destroy union labor
as it now exists; and

"WHEREAS, one of our brothers, with utter disre-
gard for his own safety, did accept the challenge of
these forces of lawlessness and disorder and bring them
to justice and punishment; therefore be it

"RESOLVED, by this state Federation of Labor in
convention assembled, that we extend our hearty thanks

to the brother who did render this great service to our cause; and be it further

"RESOLVED, that a medal of suitable design be struck in his honor, and presented to him as a memorial to this occasion, and that a replica of said medal shall be prominently displayed in every union hall in the state as a reminder to all loyal brothers that the cause of labor is just, and must ever be supported with the same unselfish courage and devotion that was displayed in this instance. The brother whom we are so privileged to honor is the delegate to this convention from the Building Trades Council of the city of Centerville and——."

There was a lot of applause, and the reading of the resolution was never completed; but by the time the delegates had finished riding me around the hall on their shoulders there was no doubt as to who was meant. Because of the hullabaloo no one remembered to appoint a committee to procure the medal, nor were any funds ever appropriated to defray the expense.

CHAPTER 42

Labor Rampant

THE tenth anniversary of my arrival in Centerville found me on the crest of the wave. I was one of the acknowledged labor leaders in the state, and since the Weaver episode no one had challenged my rule in Centerville. It had been found impractical for me to hold an important office in the State Federation of Labor, for that took a lot of time and no real benefit resulted. I gave Mike all my backing, and he made an ideal president. I saw him once a month, and nothing in the world could keep him from telling me every single thing of importance that had happened in state labor circles since our last visit. In fact, he was ten times as good as a full-time operator when it came to getting and delivering information.

The end of the boom, and the arrival of depression brought evil days to Centerville, to the Chief, and to me. In addition to having my income drastically reduced, I soon saw the savings of fifteen years wiped out. I had invested everything in real estate, all of it heavily mortgaged.

The organized labor movement was dead on its feet. Hundreds of locals remained in existence simply because the annual reports of the international unions were discouraging enough as it was, without the addition of a wholesale cancellation of charters. I doubt if there had been twenty men initiated into labor unions in our state for a year.

My business, the labor spy business, was a good reflection of all business. We were busy when the manufacturers were busy, and when they started to economize one of the first things to be discontinued was the expenditure for espionage. I couldn't blame them. With business in the doldrums only skeleton crews of the oldest and best men were retained in the shops. Such men needed little watching.

When the Blue Eagle first appeared on the horizon, organized labor instinctively sensed a friend and protector. Almost over night it seemed as if half the shops in town were striking. I got a frantic call from the Chief. The president of the manufacturers' association had phoned him and insisted that these outbursts on the part of labor be stopped at once. Expense be damned! Stop these strikes and stop them immediately! I was to be put back on my old salary.

"Chief," I said when he had passed these instructions on to me, "have you any ideas as to how I might stop some of these strikes?"

"Is that a question to ask me?" he shouted. "You've

been in the business nearly twenty years and you ask me how to settle strikes. Get to work and stop them, and we'll figure out a plan afterwards."

It was easy enough for the Chief to talk this way, but these strikes were different from any I had ever seen before. There was neither rime nor reason to most of them. The old-style strike was brought about by the local union to which the employees belonged. The lodge met, and a motion was made to the effect that a strike would be called if certain demands were not acceded to by a certain time. If the motion carried, and the company failed to agree to the terms submitted, the strike became effective.

In Centerville I had arranged things so that no strike could have the official sanction of organized labor unless the executive committee of the Central Labor Union approved it. The night the Chief called me, there were sixteen strikes in town that I knew of. The Central Labor Union had no information on a single one of them. As near as I could find out only three of these strikes had any connection whatsoever with any of our local unions. And the three strikes by union men had started without the knowledge or consent of the officers of the three locals. The Chief's suggestion was as good as any, "Stop them, and we'll figure out a plan afterwards." I was able to stop a few of them, but we never found a plan that was any good.

One of our plants was a subsidiary of a nation-wide concern, and there was a strike at the company's main factory a thousand miles away. When the employees of the local plant arrived for work one morning they found four men picketing the gate with banners announcing a strike, and the workmen were afraid to go in. The men congregated in a nearby vacant lot. Some unknown speaker addressed them, and they elected a shop committee of their own. I got wind of this at noon, and went to the scene. After searching high and low I could find no one who knew the identity of the committee, what the strike was about, or anything else, except that only thirty out of four hundred hands had gone in to work. This condition existed for a day, and then I found the committee.

"I am chairman of the organizing committee of the Central Labor Union," I said by way of introduction. "I heard you are on strike and I came out to offer the assistance of organized labor."

The committee looked at me askance. They had never heard of the CLU, and knew nothing about labor unions. Their company had been one of the strongholds of the open shop for thirty years. They welcomed me after a fashion, and I asked them to tell me just what they were striking for. None of the five men were certain, but at last they said the strike was to make the company agree to the NRA code for the industry.

Lord deliver us! The code was not yet written—it had not even been started. I got the committee to meet the plant manager, and frankly tell him they had been stampeded by a group of outsiders, and this actually seemed to be the case. They went back to work. This settled one strike, but it seemed that every strike we managed to stop was replaced by at least two more in other shops.

These strikes were a nightmare to me. Few men in the country had more actual experience in the manipulation of labor unions than I had. The Chief had supervised more labor crises, but I had the greater experience when it came to going out on the firing line and putting the deals across. Under the NRA, both of us were lost in a land where none of our tried and true rules worked at all. We were like operators on a large electric control board that had gone haywire. We pushed and pulled the right switches, but nothing happened the way it should. If we closed a switch for the purpose of lighting green lights, we got a flare of pink and yellow. Here is an example:

The Central Labor Union was having its regular bimonthly meeting. The guard came in to announce, "Three guys who say they're from the Atlas Manufacturing Co. They've got a union there, and they want to join the CLU."

"Go back and ask them if their union is affiliated with the American Federation of Labor," I said in my official capacity as presiding officer.

"No, they say they just had a meeting yesterday and formed a union and thought they would come down and get acquainted," was the reply brought back.

"Tell the delegation that this is an organization composed of delegates from AFL locals only," I responded with dignity. "If they will procure a charter from the international union of their craft, we will be glad to seat their delegates on the presentation of the proper credentials."

"Hey, wait a minute," said the fresh young delegate from the newly organized Building Service Employees' Union. "If these guys have got a union, let's take them in and then get the charter. We'll get it for them if they don't know how. I heard about that bunch. They got together yesterday and staged a strike that lasted only about an hour, and they got all they asked for. They're real fighters and that's what we need in here. I move we ask them to come in and talk things over."

There were a dozen seconds and I had to put the motion to a vote. It was carried unanimously. The three Atlas men were admitted. In spite of all I could do the organizing committee (with myself still chairman and powerless) wrote a letter to the machinists' union asking for a charter, and in a few days they got it. As president of the CLU, I had to swear in the officers of the new lodge, and give it my official blessing. It all happened so quickly that the three operators we had in the plant were unable to stop it.

Plants with well established company unions had less labor trouble under the NRA than those lacking this protection. Hundreds of firms without this defense hastened to organize their employees into some sort of association with the usual representation plan, benefits, insurance, etc. It was fondly hoped that union organizers would lose interest in the face of such defense as of yore, but this was no longer the case.

[282]

The Chief had orders for hundreds of operators to assist in these programs, and several of the plants in Centerville came to him for help. The program followed at the oil refinery several years before was almost identical with the efforts we made to head off the NRA union drives. By this time, however, the "yellow dog" contract had been declared illegal. Without it membership certificates in a company union were almost worthless as a means of controlling employees.

Another difficulty we encountered was in securing good operators. Hundreds of our best men had drifted away during the depression, and couldn't be traced. It takes months to train a man to be a real shop leader. These company union jobs had to be completed in a matter of weeks, and the Chief told me the work done by some of the greenhorns he was forced to employ was simply pathetic. Many of them fluked, others got turned up through ignorance, and a large number were simply ineffective. But still the employers kept clamoring, "Help us. We can't operate if a labor union gets control of our people. Give us protection. Preserve our property. Damn the expense—keep the unions out of our plants at any price."

I had little to do with any of these company-union campaigns because of the endless hours I was spending in an effort to keep in touch with the enormous volume of AFL activity in the city and state. But we were fighting a losing battle all along the line.

Nearly every industry had a lot to say at that time about

[283]

the benefits or abuses to which it was subjected under the NRA. I don't believe any other industry in the land obtained more business as a direct result of the Blue Eagle than we did; and I am equally sure that no other industry had any more trouble.

CHAPTER 43

Finis

I SHALL always think of Wednesday of the second week
of the 1935 convention as marking the beginning of
the end of the American Federation of Labor, but possibly
it was a rebirth.

It was well known that resolutions dealing with the proposal that the AFL change from the horizontal to the vertical type of unionism would provide the most serious work
of the convention. Despite his convictions, President Green,
as fair a man as I have ever known, put every man on the
resolutions committee who was really qualified to make
recommendations on the subject, regardless of which side
he was on. At one time or another I have known most of
these members, and they are the finest, most sincere men
in American life today, and this goes for the stand-patters
as well as the progressives. Several times I have remarked
on the oratorical ability of labor officials. Never was it so

apparent as on this occasion. Several men spoke extemporaneously for over an hour, and few audiences have ever heard subjects presented with greater clarity or understanding.

The issue was never in doubt, however, and at midnight the AFL decided to adhere to the craft system of unionism by a vote of two to one. A large number of delegates had been instructed by their international unions to sustain the old system, but there were a lot of them who really were in favor of a change, and weren't backward about saying so, somewhat along these lines: "It's a mistake. This will drive the miners, and the typos, and the ladies'-garment workers, and the brewers out of the AFL; and we can't do business without them."

But none of this is my story. The following day something occurred that was of much more immediate interest to me. A resolution was read that, after droning on through various "Whereases," ended with:

"RESOLVED, That this Convention instruct the incoming Executive Board to take such steps as may be necessary or expedient to call the attention of Congress to the new dangers which the activity of the 'labor spy,' or anti-union under-cover agency, now present, and, be it further

"RESOLVED, That the American Federation of Labor shall request that a special Congressional Investigation of the anti-labor activities of private detective and similar agencies shall be held as quickly as legislation to that end can be enacted."

FINIS

Several delegates spoke on the subject. Their remarks indicated a complete lack of exact knowledge but the hue and cry was started. I felt the impulse to demand recognition and shout, "Brothers, forget the investigation. For ten grand, I'll put every labor spy agency in the country out of business."

Union men often talked about the spy menace but did little about it. I often thought that if they had hired a smart detective and turned him loose on the spy companies he could have turned up so many operators that a thousand employers would have lost their nerve and canceled their contracts. No, the AFL would rather spend its money sending fraternal delegates to Europe, erecting office buildings, organizing an insurance company, and wasting time in a half-baked effort to organize the southern textile mills.

I sat there until the session adjourned and everyone had gone. Finally I shuffled out and walked up to the Steel Pier, and then back to my hotel. I found a note there from Mike asking me to join him and the missus for dinner at Hackney's that night. I carefully folded the paper and placed it in my wallet. It is my only souvenir of a great guy. I never saw him again.

I had seen the handwriting on the wall and I needed no one to translate it for me. It seemed to say, "The jig is up. Get out now while the getting is good. A national investigation will be a Roman holiday." The day of the labor spy who gained his ends by finesse and not fisticuffs was ended.

The train from the east gets to Centerville about noon.

[287]

By one o'clock I had loaded my car with such personal belongings as I could carry, drawn what little money I had from the bank, and started. I congratulated myself on having resigned from the National Guard several months before. You can't run away from the Guard without getting caught sooner or later.

At the corner of my street I stopped and looked both directions. At last I turned to the right for no particular reason. Northtown was on the route. I saw the old building where Jerry and I had set up shop years ago when we beat the Mutual Benefiters to the draw. There was a banner across the gate at Union field announcing a football game the following Saturday between the Northtown team and the team from the refinery where I had hooked MC-311 and 317.

While waiting for the traffic light, I noticed a Western Union office. I called to the messenger boy who idled in the doorway and he brought me a pad of blanks. For the first time in my life I wrote a telegram without counting the words in advance to see if there were more than ten.

"YOU SAID I HAD DONE EVERYTHING AN OPERATOR CAN DO EXCEPT FLUKE STOP BY THE TIME YOU GET THIS I WILL BE ONE HUNDRED PER CENT

"GT-99."

CHAPTER 44

Anticlimax—July 1, 1937

TWENTY years learning a trade that no longer exists.
There was a senatorial investigation, several of them
in fact. Labor, the New Deal and the heir to the Progressive
Party rode roughshod over industrial espionage from one
end of the docket to the other. I am glad I got out when
I did.

I decided to make use of my only remaining talent. I've
written from six to ten million words of copy in the past
twenty odd years, and it should have taught me something
about the art of story-telling.

I advise labor union readers not to search their memory
for the identity of anyone I have mentioned here, or to ran-
sack union records for the incidents I have related. Every
individual in this book actually lived, and every incident
took place. But can you blame me for camouflaging them
to the extent that no one will suffer unnecessary embarrass-
ment?

On numerous occasions clients have marveled at the ease with which workingmen and their leaders were manipulated by me or other operators. Readers may be similarly incredulous—so I will relate the axioms on which our work was founded. People are generally the same the world over. There are only two classes: the plodder who is content with his job and his home (so long as he has both), and the man with some degree of ambition. Many laboring men—as well as bank clerks, actors or school teachers—will stand an almost unbelievable amount of pushing around before they even think of risking their positions and comforts by fighting back. These are the plodders. The chaps with ambition are handled in a different manner—but handled just the same. One offers them a little reward, or even graft, and they fall in line. Such simple tactics have been used by politicians (and union leaders) for many years, and we merely adopted the idea.

My Canadian farm is uncommonly peaceful. Yes, I moved over here last fall. The only disturbance is afforded by the arrival of the weekly supply of newspapers from the States. They came in this morning. It seems that the spot news has to do with labor. Somehow my interest lags when I read the wild tales under the screaming heads on all the front pages, and particularly as regards the leadership and personnel of the CIO. A lot of this stuff seems without rime or reason.

For example: I was hooking coal miners all over District Number 2 of the United Mine Workers' Union in 1927-28.

This represents central and western Pennsylvania. There was a strike, and what a strike! The Union was hanging on to its few remaining locals with a death grip; the strike had been lost and they were trying to save the pieces. The men I hooked were slowly but surely breaking up some of the locals, but the most destructive force was the "Save the Miners' Union" movement. This was an insurgent creation under the guidance of Johnny Brophy, Pat Toohey and Hi-Power Hapgood. They were fighting John L. Lewis and his union tooth-and-nail, and Lewis was fighting back. Day after day, night after night, these two contending forces hurled incriminations at each other, and meetings and conventions frequently turned into pitched battles. In the end, the "saviours" took refuge in flight.

A year or two later, in Illinois, I crossed the trail of Brophy and Hapgood again. They were engaged in organizing a new outfit known as The National Miners' Union. The NMU was affiliated with the Trade Union Unity League. William Z. Foster allegedly ruled the TUUL, and he was also the secretary of the Communist Party, U. S. A. Lewis was again fighting Brophy and Hapgood, with no quarter given and none asked. In other words, ten years ago, John L. Lewis was battling for his very existence against these men.

If today's newspapers stated that Stalin and Hitler had gone fishing together would you believe it? Or that Mussolini had requested the lord high mogul of all the Freemasons to visit Italy and assist him in governing it? Or that the Duke of Windsor was week-ending with the Baldwins?

Well, that's the way the story of John L. Lewis's presently reported association with Brophy, Hapgood, and Toohey looks to me. It couldn't happen, that's all. And they tell me that the CIO and Lewis have been adopted by the *New Masses* and the *Daily Worker*. That is more proof of the utter absurdity of the situation. I'm now prepared to read that William Randolph Hearst and Ham Fish have been appointed general CIO organizers. On my next trip to New York I'm going to pay a visit to East 13th Street, and if the Communist party can still be found I'm going to ask Bob Minor, or Ike Amter, or Louie Engdahl to tell me what it's all about. If they admit CIO connections, I'll know for a certainty that the millennium is actually approaching.

In spite of all this I have a lingering affection for the CIO. It will give the American workman a bad beating, but he has it coming to him. The American public has never been what the economists call "class conscious." There has never been any general desire on the part of workers to band together for either offensive or defensive purposes. The AFL offered conservative leadership in this regard for many years, but the workers as a class turned their backs on it. Now, coincident with a perfect hysteria of desire on the part of everyone to join something, the CIO, like the pied piper, comes to lure them on with sweet refrains and wild promises. How many individuals among the thousands who are rushing into the CIO fold have asked:

"Who is John L. Lewis?

"What is his labor record?

"Who are his associates?

"Where did they come from?

"What is to be the ultimate organization of the CIO?

"Will the CIO unions be autonomous?

"Will CIO union officers be elected by an honest popular vote, or will elections be accompanied by stories similar to the ones that followed the John L. Lewis-John Brophy campaign for the presidency of the United Mine Workers about ten years ago? [This is a particularly good question to ask.]

"If John L. Lewis becomes dissatisfied with the leadership of officers of a CIO union, will he be permitted to replace them with 'provisional' officers, as was his custom in the districts of his own union for many years?

"If the CIO agreement with the mine operators permits the operators to mine and ship coal to their customers without restriction or reservation, does the CIO consider it a violation of this contract when a miners' strike is called to prevent the shipment of coal to struck steel plants?

"Why does the CIO insist on signed contracts, when it openly violates its own signed contract as described above?

"The president of a steel company refused to sign a CIO contract on the grounds that the CIO is not a responsible

[293]

party. What references can the CIO or its officials produce to refute this charge?"

This sounds like a damning indictment, but a man who is considering joining the church, or getting married, or buying a refrigerator might be expected to ask roughly equivalent questions before he committed himself. Why doesn't he do the same thing when joining a labor union?

But after all, the CIO is only slightly more ruthless than the AFL. Several of the larger AFL unions were run with a hand as heavy as that wielded by Lewis himself. Other union presidents prayed in vain for the power to do the same thing. Union leadership, like political leadership, is a matter of expediency. Our national political leadership has swung to the left. What is more natural than for a real labor leader (and John L. Lewis is that) to direct his parade in the same direction? I am convinced that right now the AFL executive committee spend an hour each day kicking themselves for not having got on the band wagon when they had the chance. For that matter, the Republican Party probably spends all of ten hours each day kicking *it*self for not having thought up a New Deal of its own before the Democrats did. That's human nature and it can't be helped.

Yes, it's decidedly peaceful here. The old fellow who lives on the next place thinks I am a broken-down machinist and that I moved to the country to regain my health. In a way, I guess he's right.

GLOSSARY

AFL, The American Federation of Labor: Organized in 1881 as an alliance of trade and labor unions for the purpose of promoting the sale of union label goods, securing favorable legislation and influencing public opinion in favor of organized labor. It also encourages the formation of local Trade and Labor unions and the combination of such unions in every city and state into self-governing bodies. The constitution specifically recognizes the autonomy of each trade, which indicates a definite policy of horizontal unions as opposed to the vertical (CIO) plan of organization.

AFL. departments: For the greater development of the labor movement, departments within the Federation have been established as follows: building trades, metal trades, railway employees and "union-label trades."

Bargaining, collective: Negotiation by a union with an employer for the labor of its members. The principle on which organized labor is founded.

[295]

Bargaining, individual: Making individual workmen's agreements between employees and employers. The antithesis of collective bargaining.

Brother: The invariable form of address used by union men when addressing or referring to each other.

Business agent: Local union official who conducts the business between his union and employers with whom union agreements are in effect. Formerly known as a "walking delegate."

Card, union: Issued to union members as evidence of their affiliation with a local union. When a member leaves the jurisdiction of his home local, he is given a "traveling" card. If he desires to work within the jurisdiction of another local of his union, he files or "deposits" his card with the secretary of that local. When a union member is expelled or suspended, his card is "lifted." When a member resigns, his card is "dropped."

Central Labor Union (CLU): See Union, Central Labor.

Charter: The document issued to a local union authorizing its existence. Federal union charters are issued by the AFL. Trades union local charters are issued by the national or international union of each trade.

Check-off: A clause in a union agreement whereby an employer deducts union dues and assessments from the wages given to an employee and turns the money over to the union treasurer. The United Mine Workers' Union has demanded this clause in contracts wherever possible, and, as this union is the backbone of the CIO, it may be assumed that the "check-off" will eventually appear in CIO contracts.

CIO, Committee for Industrial Organization: Founded in 1936 by John L. Lewis, president of the United Mine Workers of America, one of the strongest international unions. The purpose of the committee is to organize workers of each industry along industrial (vertical), instead of craft (horizontal) lines. The CIO seems to have no constitution nor any established system showing the relationship of the chief officials to the affiliated units. It is reported that John L. Lewis is chairman, Charles P. Howard, secretary, and John Brophy, director. Howard is president of the International Typographical Union, an AFL affiliate. Brophy is an old-time member of the United Mine Workers. He left that union because of trouble with Lewis some ten years ago.

Communist: A member of the Communist Party. *Life* (1937) states that there are forty-five thousand Party members in the United States—probably a sixty per cent exaggeration [GT-99]. Before calling a person a Communist, it might be well to find out if he accepts and practices the doctrine of Karl Marx as interpreted by Lenin and Stalin—but not by Trotzky.

Company union: See Union, company.

Contract, "yellow dog": An individual agreement between employer and employee whereby the latter may not join a labor organization which is not approved by the employer. This effectively prevents membership in a trade or labor union. The "yellow dog" contract has become illegal.

Council, Building Trades: Usually organized by the building trades local unions in each city for the purpose of promoting the interests of the unions engaged in the building industry.

Cover: The ostensible reason adopted by a spy or detective for his presence at the scene of activity. In shop espionage, a job in the plant is the "cover." When employed as an "outside man," an operator frequently procures employment as a salesman on a commission basis, which permits him to suit his hours of work to his sleuthing activities. GT-99's real-estate connection was his "cover."

Craft Union: See Union, craft.

Fair: When an employer has an agreement with one or more unions, his plant is said to be "fair."

[298]

Federal union: See Union, federal.

Fink: A strike-breaker or strike guard. When finks are taken to a struck shop, some are assigned to work in the plant, while others are assigned to guard the property and the workers from assault by the strikers.

Grand Lodge: A national or international union.

Guard: See Strike-breakers.

Hooking: The act of a detective agency which engages an employee of a company for the purpose of furnishing information relative to the activity of the other workers. This is resorted to when it is impossible to effect the employment of one of the agency's own operators to serve in a similar capacity. Also known as "roping."

Horizontal union: See Union, horizontal.

Industrial union: See Union, industrial.

International union: See Union, international.

Label trades: A group of unions whose agreements provide for affixing an inconspicuous label to all goods manufactured by their members as evidence of production under

[299]

"fair" conditions. Such labels are often found in hats, shoes, clothing and as paper tags stuck on loaves of bread. The printing trades also use a label. It will be found on all political announcements or advertising, as politicians can be counted on to patronize only union printers. At union meetings a prize is sometimes given to the man who can display the largest number of union labels on his clothing. GT-99 won such a prize by displaying a total of thirteen labels.

Labor, State Federation of: Similar to a CLU but having jurisdiction over an entire state.

Labor union: See Union, labor.

Laborite: One active in union affairs.

Laborskate: A contemptuous term applied to a union man who is suspected of using his position for personal advancement.

Local union: See Union, local.

Lockout: The act of an employer when he closes his plant to his employees pending the settlement of a dispute. The antithesis of a strike.

National Union: See Union, national.

Operator or *operative:* The labor spy's term for members of his profession.

Organize: To recruit members for a union.

Organizer: A man employed for the purpose of forming new local unions or augmenting the strength of existing ones. Many of the larger unions have a crew of organizers who work on a regular salary. The AFL also has a force of organizers who are assigned to assist member unions or to handle special situations such as the unsuccessful effort to unionize the southern cotton mill and steel workers in 1930. A number of AFL organizers were assigned to this task but nothing came of it.

Outside man: A spy with a roving commission assigned to a city or state where he gains the confidence of labor leaders and reports their plans and actions to his clients. GT-99 was an "outside man" during most of his career. Other "outside men" have retained their positions for as many as thirty years, taking an increasingly active part, not only in labor matters but in political and fraternal circles, all of which enhances the value of the spy to his employers.

Picket: A striker who is assigned to patrol the vicinity of a struck shop for the purpose of keeping workers from entering the plant and to inform the public that a strike

[301]

exists. A multitude of laws define and limit the rights
of pickets. Because of this protection by a liberal government, unions have gone to such extremes that pickets, in
the larger cities at least, are a good deal of a joke and subject to ridicule. A good way to gauge a strike is to ask
a picket what he is striking for. If he can give you a
half-way sensible answer he is far above the average. It
is not uncommon in large cities for union officials to
demand recognition from an employer whose people have
no connection with, or desire to join a union. If the employer refuses, his shop is picketed to force compliance.
At one time the employer could obtain a court injunction
against such interference, but labor legislation has made
this difficult.

Roping: See Hooking.

Scab: A union man who continues to work when a strike
has been called by his union. The term, however, is generally applied to any employee, whether union or non-
union, who works in a struck shop.

Shop, Closed: A shop operating under a union agreement
covering wages, hours and conditions, and employing
union workers exclusively. The term "shop" applies to
any place of employment; steamship, mine, store, bus
line, factory, etc.

Shop, open: A shop with no union agreement.

Shop, preferential: A shop agreeing to union wages and conditions and giving preference to union men but not required to employ them exclusively.

Spotter: In espionage parlance, a spy or operator who rides as a passenger on trains, busses or street-cars to detect dishonesty on the part of the conductor or other members of the crew. Also known as a checker. Workmen often designate any labor spy as a "spotter."

Spy, labor: A representative of a detective agency who secures work in a shop, factory, mine, office, transportation system or other place of employment for the purpose of procuring information relative to the personal activity of the other employees. The primary mission of a labor spy is to report all acts of sabotage, nepotism, union activity, favoritism, dishonesty, waste, and incompetency. Information of a constructive nature for the improvement of production and the supervision of personnel is equally important. A very few spies, such as GT-99, work on the "outside."

Five major firms are known to have been engaged in this business prior to 1937. GT-99 estimates the maximum number of operators employed by each to have been five hundred or a total of twenty-five hundred. The average charge for an operator is eight dollars per working day or $2400 per annum. The gross yearly business done by these companies on this basis would total $6,000,000. Several of these firms also engaged in criminal detective work which had no connection with the industrial part of the business. And this estimate does not include the cost of espionage by firms which handled such matters without outside assistance. The author believes that one-half of the total number of operators, 1250, were members of labor organizations. In 1936 the AFL claimed a total of 33,820 locals. On this basis it is quite probable that not more than one local out of 27 numbered a spy among its members.

The radical *New Masses* in June 1937 comments on the 1936-37 labor spy investigation by a Senatorial Committee, stating: "There are some 41,000 union locals in the U. S. and *there is a spy in every local* . . . $175 a month paid to the agency per spy, and 40,000 spies, computes the minimum cost at over $80,000,000 per year." These figures are attributed to "Mr. Heber Blankenhorn, industrial economist on the National Labor Relations Board." His estimation of the number of locals differs by about 6,000 from AFL 1936 figures, but his greatest error is the assumption that there is a "spy in every local." Who in the world would pay for the services of a spy in every barbers' local, or want to get the low-down on the actors, musicians, plumbers or rural letter carriers? A careful estimate reveals that one-third of the union members in the U. S. and Canada work for Federal or local governments (which seldom engage outside detectives) or are in trades where espionage is either impractical or of no advantage to employers. This includes the building trades unions among which espionage was almost unknown, for reasons given in *Labor Spy*.

The term "labor spy" is never used by the detective agencies or operators in describing their work; it was coined by the unions.

Strike benefit: Money paid to strikers from the treasury of the local union. The AFL encourages each local to build up a "war chest" to be used only in case of a strike.

Strike, sympathetic: A strike on the part of employees who have no grievances against their employer, in order to force compliance with the demands of other workers who claim a just cause for striking. If an employer has agreements with two or more unions and one union calls a strike, the other unions will sometimes strike in "sympathy" with the original strikers. Sympathetic strikes are also called in shops which buy from or furnish supplies to a struck shop.

Trade union: See Union, trade.

Union card: See Card, union.

Union, Central Labor (CLU): When five or more local unions, affiliated with the AFL, are in the same com-

[305]

munity they may organize a Central Labor Union for the purpose of generally promoting the interests of organized labor. Similar terms are Central Trades and Labor Assembly or Council, Federation of Labor, Trades Council, Central Federated Union, etc.

Union, company: The name given by unionists to employees' associations which have been organized or sponsored by company management and to which only employees of one company belong. The advocates of the trade union system claim that company unions are formed for the express purpose of preventing organization by established unions.

Union, craft: An association of workers employed in the same trade or craft. For example, carpenters, regardless of whether they are employed on construction work or in an automobile plant.

Union, federal: An isolated independent union chartered by the AFL at the request of a group of workers employed in a vocation for which no national or international union exists. For example: Russian and Turkish Bath Rubbers' and Workers' Union No. 18702, Newark, N. J.

Union, horizontal: Same as craft union.

Union, industrial: A union which endeavors to enroll all the workers employed in a given industry regardless of trade or craft. The United Mine Workers of America is such a union and it admits all employees in and around a mine such as miners, electricians, engineers, machinists, etc.

Union, international: A union with branches, or locals, in the United States and Canada. Example: The International Brotherhood of Bookbinders. Some unions have been accused of maintaining impotent locals in Canada merely to retain the "International" designation. The 1936 convention of the AFL was attended by only two Canadian delegates (out of a total of 493) which indicates the absurdity of the larger unions' claims to internationalism.

Union, labor: An organized association of workmen formed for the protection and promotion of their common interest, the ultimate purpose being to enroll all persons employed in a trade (if a craft or horizontal union) or industry (if an industrial or vertical union) and to bargain collectively for the labor of its members. Literally, a "labor union" is composed of members who are employed in an unskilled trade, such as hod carriers or longshoremen. See Union, trade.

Union label: See Label Trades.

Union, local: A branch of a national or international union, generally referred to as a local.

[307]

Union, national: A union with branches in the United States only. Example: National Brotherhood of Operative Potters.

Union recognition: Admission by an employer that a union to which some or all of his employees belong is the sole bargaining agent for the labor of said employees. Such an employer "recognizes" the union.

Union, trade: A union composed of workers who have served an apprenticeship and learned one of the crafts; machinists, lithographers, plumbers, etc. The terms "trade" union and "labor" union are often used indiscriminately, even by union people.

Union, vertical: Generally used as in LABOR SPY, as a synonym for industrial union. The CIO makes this distinction, however: "While the term vertical union is sometimes wrongly used to mean an industrial union, there is an important difference between the two. A vertical union is one that takes in all workers who contribute to the production of a certain product, from those who produce the raw material to those who make the final article. . . . A union that took in both steel workers and coal miners would be a vertical union. But that is not what the C. I. O. favors. . . . Steel and coal are different industries. The making of cloth and the use of that cloth to make garments are distinct industries. There is no need under present conditions for the industrial or semi-industrial unions in these fields to combine into a vertical organization."

Walking delegate: See Business Agent.

THE END